SPORT Science

Roy Hawkey

MA(Cantab), MA(Sc.Ed), MIBiol

Senior Lecturer and Head of Centre
Centre for Mathematics and Science Education
Brighton Polytechnic

Hodder & Stoughton

A MEMBER OF THE HODDER HEADLINE GROUP

Order: Please contact Bookpoint Ltd, 39 Milton Park, Abingdon,
Oxon OX14 4TD. Telephone: (44) 01235 400414. Fax: (44) 01235 400454.
Lines are open from 9 am - 6 pm Monday to Saturday, with a 24-hour
message answering service. Email address: orders@bookpoint.co.uk

British Library Cataloguing in Publication Data
Hawdey, Roy
  Sports Science, - 2nd ed.
  1. Sports and games. Scientific aspects
  I. Title
  796.015

ISBN 0 340 52523 1

First published 1991
Impression number   15 14 13 12 11 10 9 8 7 6 5
Year   2004 2003 2002 2001 2000 1999 1998

Typeset by Wearset, Boldon, Tyne and Wear.
Printed in Great Britain for Hodder & Stoughton Educational,
a division of Hodder Headline Plc, 338, Euston Road, London NW1 3BH
by Redwood Books, Trowbridge, Wiltshire BA14 8RN.

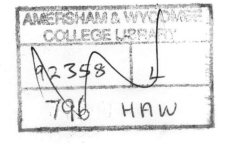

Sport Science

Acknowledgements

The Publishers would like to thank the following for permission to reproduce material in this volume:

A and C Black (Publishers) Ltd for the illustration from *Sports Training Principles*, second edition by Frank Dick (1989).

Every effort has been made to trace and acknowledge ownership of copyright. The Publishers will be glad to make suitable arrangements with any copyright holders whom it has not been possible to contact.

The Publishers would like to thank the following for permission to use their photographs in this volume:

Action Plus (20; 24, middle; 25, top; 26; 47, top; 74); Action Plus/John Babb (87, top right); Action Plus/Chris Barry (44; 47, bottom left); Action Plus/David Davies (24, bottom left); Action Plus/Richard Francis (25, middle); Action Plus/Tony Henshaw (87, bottom right); Action Plus/Mike Hewitt (46; 47, middle left; 70, top; 75; 80); Action Plus/Andrew Morris (87, bottom left); Action Plus/Lee Wardle (25, bottom); Allsport (30, left, bottom; 48; 98; 100); Allsport/Robert Beck (47, middle right); Allsport/Simon Bruty (11); Allsport/Julian Calder (87, top left); Allsport/Chris Cole (59, bottom); Allsport/Tom Hevezi (5, top); Allsport/Trevor Jones (24, top right); Allsport/Bob Martin (70, bottom); Allsport/Adrian Murrell (9); Allsport/Mike Powell (47, top; 85; 88, left); John Burles (24, top left); J Allan Cash Ltd (5, bottom; 19); Dendix Brushes Ltd (106); Dunlop Sports Co Ltd (51; 52, left); Dunlop Tyre and Rubber Co Ltd (104); John Evans and Pearl Assurance (21, right); London Foot Hospital and School of Chiropody (92, bottom); Mitre Sports Ltd (52, right); Popperfoto (37; 59, top; 101); Running Magazine/West Highland News Agency (88, right); Science Photo Library (6, lower middle right); Science Photo Library/Martin Dohrn (95); Science Photo Library/Simon Fraser, Hexham General (72); Science Photo Library/Imperial College London, Physics Dept. (6, top left); Science Photo Library/Dick Luria (6, upper middle right); Science Photo Library/St Bartholomew's Hospital (6, bottom right); Science Photo Library/Sheila Terry, Truswal Systems (6, bottom left); Science Photo Library/Jerome Yeats (6, middle left); Sporting Pictures (UK) Ltd (30, right); St Bartholomew's Hospital, Dept. of Medical Illustration (92; 93, top); Topham (21, left).

Contents

What is Sport Science?

'Move over, coach. Here come the scientists.'

So began *New Scientist*'s 1984 Olympic Special issue. But sport science does not replace the coach or trainer – although it may well help.

Sports science is the application of scientific ideas to sporting activities. It is an essential part of physical education, and can help answer the questions which may lie behind the desire to improve performance.

Is this Sport Science?

Am I the right build for my sport?
How can I use information about sport?
How can I improve my techniques?
Why do some balls bounce higher than others?
What is top-spin?
Can I react quickly enough?
How powerful are my muscles?
What are the key factors in athletics?
Where do the forces act on a cyclist?
How much effect do playing surfaces have?
How effective is practice?

These are the kinds of question which this book will try to answer. Or, at least, it will show the problems in more detail, and give some ideas

about how they might be solved. Each of the questions above is dealt with, at least to some extent, in the chapters which follow.

What is sport?

Before we go further, we need to think about what science is, and – first – what sport is.

Here is a list of recreational activities:

archery	hockey
ballet	painting
bird-watching	sailing
chess	show-jumping
cricket	skittles
crosswords	soccer
dancing	swimming
fishing	tennis
golf	volleyball
hill-walking	weight-lifting

Part of science is concerned with classifying things. As sport scientists we should be able to classify these activities into sports and pastimes. To do so we need to know what exactly we mean by the term 'sport'.

Make three lists from the activities above:

(a) those which definitely are *not* sports;
(b) those which definitely *are* sports;
(c) those which *may* or *may not* be sports.

In your first list you will have bird-watching and painting. In list (b) will be golf and tennis. But what about fishing? Is that a sport or not? It depends on what we really mean by 'sport'; it depends on exactly how we define the word.

You can, of course, simply look it up in the dictionary. But a scientist is more likely to produce a set of rules. He or she uses these to judge each activity. Only if an activity obeys all the rules can it be classified as a sport.

Now the problem is to write the rules. One example is given: you can argue about these, and try to produce your own set of rules.

A sport

(a)   involves physical activity;
(b)   is competitive;
(c)   contains a directly measured quantity, e.g. time, goals, points, distance.

Try these rules on the activities in the list.

Would your three lists have been different?

What happens to gymnastics, ice-skating, fishing and jogging if these rules are applied?

And what about synchronised swimming?

Could you change any of the rules without having to say that a disco dancing contest was a sport?

Classifying sports

Can you think of a way of putting sports into groups? Of classifying them? This should help us understand more, as the same scientific principles may well apply to similar kinds of activity. For example, tennis, squash and badminton have obvious similarities.

One way of classifying sports is:

(a)   athletic sports
(b)   ball games
(c)   'combat' sports
(d)   'target' sports
(e)   water sports
(f)   winter sports

Systems like this, though, tend to either miss out some sports, or put some in twice. This scheme, for example, can't include badminton. But, if we add 'racket games' as another group, tennis and squash will occur twice, as they are also ball games. The only way to fully classify sports is to use the method of sets, with a Venn diagram.

Classification of sports

1	Combat	8	Team
2	Target	9	Court
3	Aerofoil	10	Racket
4	Mechanical	11	Horse
5	Wheeled	12	Winter
6	Water	13	Jumping
7	Dull	14	Athletic

Odd one out

Have you ever done one of those IQ tests, where some of the questions ask, 'Which is the odd one out of . . . ?'? Thirty years ago, when these tests were very popular in schools, there was lengthy correspondence in *The Times* on a sports 'odd one out' question. The four sports to choose from were:

billiards   cricket   hockey   soccer

There was lengthy argument about which was the 'best' answer. What do you think?

Can you make out a good case for each of them?

The series of letters include answers like:

billiards : more than one ball, played on a table;
cricket : ball not put into any kind of net;
soccer : no 'hitter' used to propel the ball.

One correspondent argued that hockey must be the right answer as he couldn't think of a reason for it to be the odd one! Yet, of course, hockey is the only one listed which does not have professional players (except for ice-hockey).

Keys

Scientists, particularly biologists, often use keys to help them identify and describe things. The discussion of 'odd one out' can help us to make a key to these four sports.

1	Uses a 'hitter'	2	
	No hitter used		SOCCER
2	One ball only	3	
	More than one ball		BILLIARDS
3	Ball hit into net		HOCKEY
	Ball not hit into net		CRICKET

Can you see how the key works?

Start at '1'. Choose the line which fits the sport you are thinking of. At the end of the line is either an answer, or another number. If there is another number, move to this number, and repeat the process. When you reach a name, you have the answer.

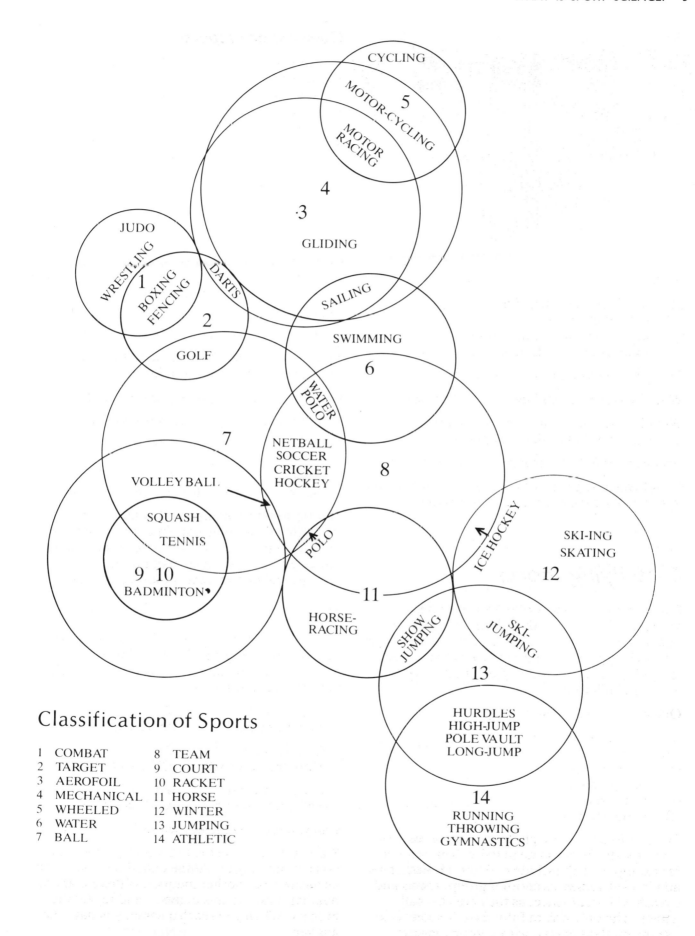

Classification of Sports

1 COMBAT
2 TARGET
3 AEROFOIL
4 MECHANICAL
5 WHEELED
6 WATER
7 BALL
8 TEAM
9 COURT
10 RACKET
11 HORSE
12 WINTER
13 JUMPING
14 ATHLETIC

Here is a similar key for football teams. It needs to be revised every four years, as teams change. This is not as easy as it seems, for you can't just replace, say West Germany with Argentina, unless their kit happens to be identical.

Key to 1990 World Cup Teams

1	Shirts and shorts same colour	2
	Shirts and shorts different	4
2	Shirts red	3
	Shirts white	UNITED ARAB EMIRATES
3	Neck trim white	SOUTH KOREA
	Neck trim red	BELGIUM
4	Shirts striped	ARGENTINA
	Shirts not striped	5
5	Shirts more than one colour	6
	Shirts one colour only (except neck trim)	7
6	Shirts mainly blue	YUGOSLAVIA
	Shirts mainly white	WEST GERMANY
7	Shirts white	8
	Shirts not white	10
8	Shorts black	AUSTRIA
	Shorts blue	9
9	Waist band red	ENGLAND
	Waist band not red	USA
10	Shirts green	11
	Shirts not green	12
11	Shorts red	CAMEROON
	Shorts white	REPUBLIC OF IRELAND
12	Shirts blue	13
	Shirts not blue	15
13	Shorts black	URUGUAY
	Shorts white	14
14	Socks blue	ITALY
	Socks red	SCOTLAND
15	Shirts orange/yellow	16
	Shirts red	20
16	Shirts orange	HOLLAND
	Shirts yellow	17
17	Socks red	18
	Socks not red	19
18	Shorts with red trim	COLUMBIA
	Shorts with white trim	ROMANIA
19	Socks white	BRAZIL
	Socks yellow	SWEDEN
20	Shorts blue	21
	Shorts white	22
21	Socks white	COSTA RICA
	Socks black	SPAIN
22	Socks white	EGYPT
	Socks not white	23
23	Socks blue	CZECHOSLOVAKIA
	Socks red	USSR

Keys like these can also be in diagram form. This one uses computer flowchart symbols.

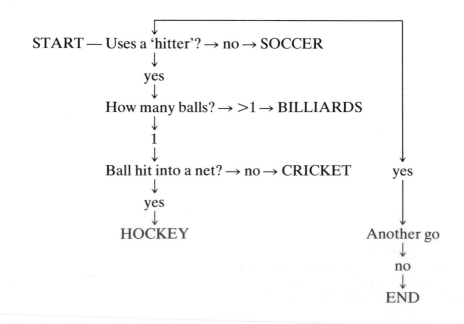

This kind of key can easily be coded in BASIC or LOGO. A version in BASIC is given here.

(Note: other computer programs in this book are indicated by the computer symbol, and listed in Appendix A, page 108.)

```
10   REM KEY © RSH 1987
20   PRINT "KEY TO BALL GAMES"
30   INPUT "Is a 'hitter' used?",A$
40   IF A$> = "Y" THEN GOTO 60
50   PRINT "SOCCER" : GOTO 120
60   INPUT "Is only 1 ball used?",B$
70   IF B$> = "Y" THEN GOTO 90
80   PRINT "BILLIARDS": GOTO 120
90   INPUT "Is ball hit into net?",C$
100  IF C$> = "Y" THEN PRINT "HOCKEY":
     GOTO 120
110  PRINT "CRICKET"
120  INPUT "Another go?",D$
130  IF  D$> = "Y"  THEN  RUN
140  END
```

Computers actually work in binary, a system of 0s and 1s. They can handle binary codes very quickly. Here are binary codes for the four sports in our key:

BILLIARDS 110

CRICKET 101

HOCKEY 111

SOCCER 011

Can you work out the code?*

Try to code for these sports:

Bowls

Polo

Are there sports for codes 010 or 100?

---

* *First digit is for hitter (1 = 'yes'); second for net (1 = 'yes'); third for number of balls (0 <> 1!)*

2

What is science?

Science is a way of finding out about things and events. Like other areas of study, it depends on observing, asking questions and collecting information. What makes science special is the use of controlled experiments to test ideas.

This diagram shows a simplified version of how science works:

Collecting information

Much of the basic, unglamorous work of science is concerned with collecting information.

Information can be collected from many different places. One technique is to use a tally-chart while watching a sporting event. In this example, a list

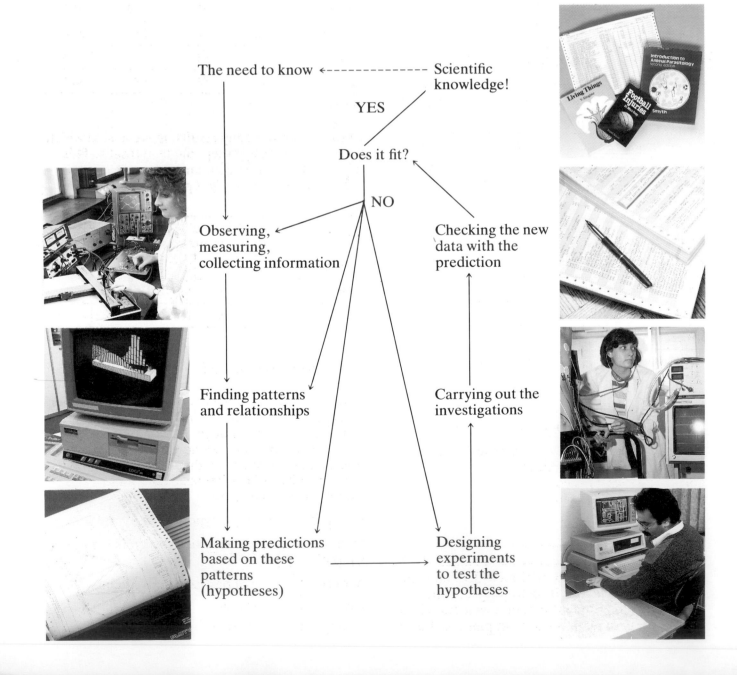

The need to know ←------------- Scientific knowledge!

YES

Does it fit?

NO

Observing, measuring, collecting information

Checking the new data with the prediction

Finding patterns and relationships

Carrying out the investigations

Making predictions based on these patterns (hypotheses)

Designing experiments to test the hypotheses

was made of events which happened during a rugby union match, and a check made each time one take place. Part of the original record looked like this:

Free kicks

||||| || 7

|||| 4

The final, completed figures were:

	IRELAND	ENGLAND
Scrums won	12	10
Scrums 'against the head'	3	0
Line-outs win	22	28
Free kicks	7	4
Penalties	8	10
Attempts at goal	1	4
Penalty goals	1	1
Tries	1	1
Conversions	1	0
Dropped goals	1	0

'Fact-finder' from a rugby union international

This sort of 'fact-finder' is often used by commentators. It can be used to record various events in a variety of sports, for example:

tennis : doublt faults, aces, first serves 'in'
soccer : corners, free-kicks
golf : holes 'birdied'
cricket : boundaries hit

Results tables

All measurements need to be recorded, and the simplest way to do this is to draw up a results table. This keeps the information well organised, tidy and easy to read. Some examples are shown.

Distance, m	0	10	20	30	40	
Time, s	0	1.9	3.7	5.1	6.4	
Distance, m	50	60	70	80	90	100
Time, s	7.6	8.7	9.8	10.9	12.0	13.1

Intervals in 100 m sprint

Attempt	1	2	3	4	5	6	7	8	9	10
Score	7	6	7	6	5	6	5	3	4	3

Practice effect

Person	Height, m	Mass, kg	Surface area, m^2	Body temp. °C
Adam	1.80	76	1.94	36.8
Brenda	1.45	50	1.38	37.1
Catharine	1.62	48	1.50	37.0
David	1.53	63	1.59	37.0
Paul	1.66	66	1.73	36.6

Body data

Before you record any results, make a table which has in it everything except the final results. This will save time, and make sure that all the data is recorded – and in the right place.

Person	Body weight, N	Step-ups Height, m	No.	Work, J	Time, s	Power, W
Frances		0.5	100			
Graham		0.5	100			
Helen		0.5	100			

Questionnaires

Some sorts of question cannot be answered either by experiment or observation. We must ask. Not just odd questions, though. If we want answers which mean anything, we need properly designed questionnaires. We need the sort of thing used in opinion polls and market research. Some examples are given here.

Checklists are a simple type:

'Tick which of these activities you think are sports:'

hockey ☐   gymnastics ☐   tennis ☐
chess ☐   soccer ☐   fishing ☐
boxing ☐   skating ☐   golf ☐

There are also questions which include an element of choice:

'Tick to show how often you play these sports:'

	Frequently	Sometimes	Never
Soccer			
Netball			
Hockey			
Squash			

Or this kind:

'Which is nearest to your view of sports centres?'

> a waste of money
> keep people off the streets
> make no difference
> a good idea
> every town should have one

Measurements

In the scientific study of sport many types of information are needed, each measured in a particular way. Each measurement, too, has its own unit. For example, speed is normally stated in metres per second. To work it out we must measure both the distance covered and the time taken.

S.I. Units

Measurement	SI unit	abbreviation
length	metre	m
mass	kilogram	kg
time	second	s
speed	metre per second	$m\,s^{-1}$ or m/s
acceleration	metre per second per second	$m\,s^{-2}$ or m/s^2
force	newton	N
work, energy	joule	J
power	watt	W

The English-speaking world has become increasingly used to the 'metric system' of measurement. Scientists have used metric units for a long time; they, and this book, use the international system of units known as Système Internationale (S.I. for short).

The table gives the common S.I. units and their abbreviations.

Apart from time with its minutes and hours, all the S.I. units have the same sets of larger and smaller relatives. For example, a kilometre (km) is 1000 metres (m), a kilojoule (kJ) is 1000 joules (J); a millimetre (mm) is 1/1000 metres, a milliwatt (mW) is 1/1000 watts (W). Less common are centi (1/100, e.g. cm) and mega (1 million, e.g. MW).

Two kinds of measurement

Disputed goal wins final

Disqualified after finishing first

CROWD BOOS JUDGES

No-jump costs title

WORLD RECORD NOT RATIFIED

WINNING GOAL IN INJURY TIME

Run out on last ball

'But the machine says it's out!'

These kinds of headline remind us that there are two types of measurement:

objective – a numerical value which can be measured by instruments or counted;

subjective – a score based mainly on the views of the judge, whatever the guidelines may be.

Let's look at some examples; try to decide whether each 'measurement' is objective or subjective.

(a)   a long jump of 7.95 m
(b)   football result, 3–2
(c)   figure-skating score, 7.8
(d)   a round of golf in 72 strokes

(e)   a boxer winning on 'points'
(f)   a gymnast scoring 9.7
(g)   a swim taking 53.8 s
(h)   a snooker break of 84

In some sports, objective measurement is straightforward, counting strokes or goals. In others, the measurement is objective, given the problems already discussed: times and distances. A third group of sports has a largely subjective scoring system. Some of these, such as figure-skating, even give points for 'artistic impression'. In these sports, no single judge's score is 'correct', and an average is taken.

Look through the list of sports on page 1, and find others which have some subjective measurement.

Even in the most objective sports, though, there are subjective decisions to make. Referees, umpires and judges have only a fraction of a second to decide whether a ball or toe was over a line, or whether time was 'up', or whether a player was offside, or . . . The measurement may be objective, but it is a subjective decision as to whether it should be made at all.

Accuracy and errors

Suppose everyone in the class has a stop-watch, and times the same event. Would you expect them to record exactly the same time?

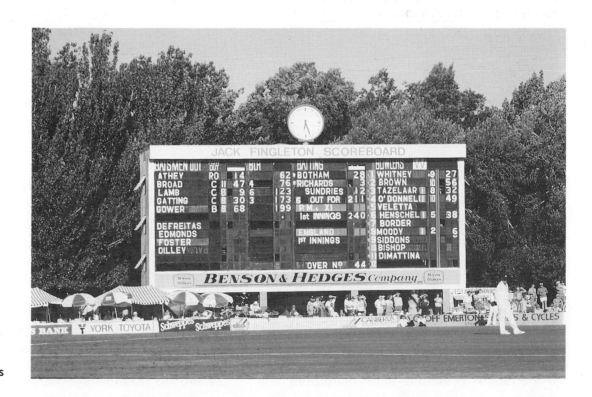

Cricket umpires have to make both objective and subjective decisions

No. There would be several reasons for errors, some faster, some slower. See how many you can think of.

You probably thought of reasons like these:

(a) errors in the watches themselves;
(b) human error – too early or too late in starting or stopping the watch;
(c) viewing error – not everybody could be exactly in line with the finish;
(d) inaccuracy in reading the watch, especially if between two markings.

Digital stop watch

Disagreement or error?

In fact, there are errors in the best scientific measurements. The main point is to know that they exist, and to try to avoid them, or to make allowances for them. Let's look at a few examples.

At a normal athletics meeting – we'll come to the Olympics later – the timekeepers stand or sit alongside the finishing line. It didn't take long to find out that the times for 400 m races and longer were much more accurate than those for the sprints. There were two reasons for this. Look at the track diagram, and try to think of them.

One reason is purely mathematical, 100 m takes about 10 s; 10000 m takes about half an hour. An error of 0.1 s makes a lot of difference in 10 s, very little in 1800 s! The longer the race, the less important a very small error is. To be as inaccurate as 0.1 s in the 100 m would mean an error of nearly 1½ minutes in the marathon!

The second reason is more scientific. When starting pistols were first used (before then it was flags), watches were started as soon as the shot was *heard*; now they are started when smoke from the gun is *seen*. The speed of sound in air is about 300 m/s; the speed of light is 300 000 000 m/s. Sound takes 0.3 s to travel 100 m; light takes virtually no time at all. To make things worse, it is the shortest races which start furthest away from the timekeepers.

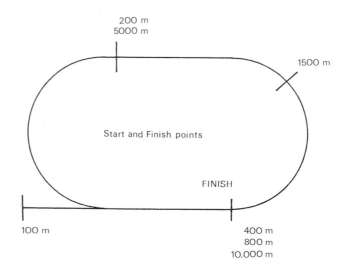

Modern electronic watches are extremely accurate, but this is no help if the timekeeper doesn't start and stop it at the exact instant. Electronic timing, as used in all major athletics and swimming events, removes the human timekeeper altogether. The clock starts automatically as the gun is fired, and stops as the finishing line is crossed.

Measuring distances, too can suffer from both mechanical and human error. The height of a jump will be inaccurate if the bar or ruler is bent, or if the judge is not tall enough to see clearly, or even if the ground is uneven. Again, modern technology has removed both kinds of error, at least in important competitions.

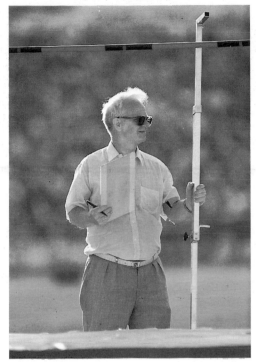

Measuring the high jump

Predicting in science and sport

Having collected the information we should, as scientists, try to explain it, by finding a pattern. Then we test our ideas by trying to predict future events, either in an experiment, or in the real world. For example, we might notice that sport was disrupted by very cold winters in 1947, 1963 and 1979. Rather like an IQ test, we predict that the same 16-year interval will make 1995 also a bad winter:

1947   1963   1979   1995?   ?   ?

Sometimes, to check a theory, we don't have to wait so long. We can use information that we already have. Football supporters often say that matches between nearby clubs (local 'derbies') are often draws. They suggest various reasons for this, such as reduced travelling, more supporters and so on. It is quite easy to investigate the 'prediction' that more of these 'derby' games are drawn:

	Number	Draws	%
Local 'derbies'	48	14	29
Others	414	118	29

Data from League Division I.
Are local 'derbies' more often drawn?

This might, the scientist would say, be a freak result. So we had better check other results, from other seasons and other divisions. Some other examples are given.

Fixture	Division	H	A	D
Norwich v Ipswich	I	5	3	3
Bradford C. v Barnsley	4	5	I	5
Rangers v Celtic	Sc. Prem.	9	3	5
Darlington v Doncaster	4	5	4	3
Liverpool v Everton	I	4	3	6

Other 'derby' results

Gambling

Predicting the results of sports events is bigger business even than the sports themselves. Horse racing and soccer attract the largest amount of gambling.

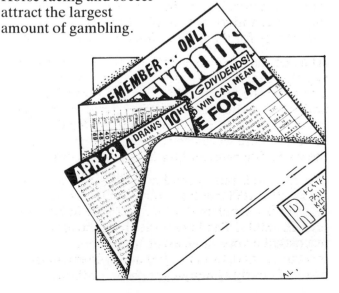

So vital are the football pools felt to be, that a 'Pools Panel' meets to invent results if league games are postponed.

A careful check of pools forecasts in newspapers suggests that they are no more accurate than any random method – sticking in pins, cathedral cities, birthdays etc. – of predicting drawn matches. If there are 8 drawn games, the odds against predicting them all are over 1 000 000 000 to 1!

A sport science experiment

The sport scientist, like other kinds of scientist, must do experiments to make discoveries. The ideas for these experiments may come from many different places: first-hand observation, articles in newspapers, remarks by commentators, or odd questions.

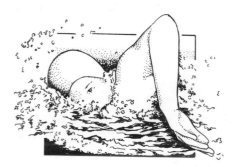

Why, for example, have many male swimmers taken to wearing swimming-caps? Or even shaving their heads completely?

Is it just that long hair gets in the way? Or does the very presence of hair affect the body's flow through the water? If it does affect the flow, we ought to be able to measure a difference between swimming with a cap, and swimming without one.

But how do we set up such an experiment? Here's a discussion among a group of students about this problem and all the factors and difficulties involved:

ADRIAN: Can we just find two swimmers, one who always wears a cap, and one who never does? Then we could compare their performances.

SALLY: No – there'll be too many other differences. We might choose a complete beginner and an Olympic champion! We can only look at one difference: cap or no cap.

CAROL: Perhaps we should use two *groups* of people, and average their results. Is this any good?

MIKE: No, again. It is better, though; individual differences will be smaller. But it still could be that all the good swimmers were in one group.

TONY: Let's *make* our swimmers wear caps or not – rather than let them choose for themselves.

SALLY: That's better. Now we can rule out the possibility that choice may be something to do with ability. Perhaps coaches tell their best pupils to wear caps, or something.

SUE: Well, just in case, what if we choose our two groups at random, ...

LEE: . . . . and make one group swim with caps first, then the other?

MIKE: Good idea. Can we go any further, make any more improvements?

JILL: Could we compare each group's performance, with and without caps?

SAM: Why stop at 2 groups, why not 3? Or 10?

MIKE: We've only got a couple of hours, Sam. And, anyway, who's going to work out the results? You?

SALLY: Isn't there another way, with just one swimmer? Get him or her to swim alternately with and without cap, then compare the times. What's wrong with that?

TONY: That seems too easy. What do you think, Graham?

GRAHAM: It might seem to be the best way of avoiding the individual differences. But the very fact that people are different means that any results might not be true for anyone else. So, the group method is much better. Scientists would call the two groups 'experimental' – with the caps, and 'control' – without, 'normal'.

Changing them over, like Lee suggests, is a good way of ruling out any other factors.

It's always important in science to be sure that we are measuring what we think we are measuring. Then we can make judgements and recommendations. If you think about them carefully, you will find that some of the experiments in this book are not perfect!

Practice makes perfect?

There is often argument about whether sportsmen are born or made. Some people certainly have better 'ball sense' or excellent muscle co-ordination. Some are physically stronger than others; some can run faster. The question we need to answer is, 'How far can practice improve performance?'

Practice has two separate aspects: results and techniques. We can practise a sports skill so that our results improve, despite a strange technique. Or we can try to perfect our technique, so that better results should follow eventually, if not at once. Here are some simple ways of investigating the effects of practice.

Tennis serve

1 Serve a number of balls on a tennis court
2 Score points for each serve that:

bounces before the net	0
lands in the net	1
is over, but long *and* wide	2
is over, but long *or* wide	3
is a 'let' service	4
is a good service	5

3 Draw a graph of the scores for each attempt
4 Try again on other days and find out whether there is any lasting improvement.

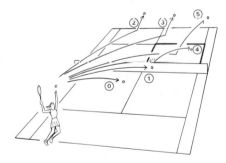

Training

The terms 'practice' and 'training' are often used as if they mean exactly the same thing. Certainly, the techniques of training – squat thrusts, weights, chins etc. – can be practised, like any technique. But the emphasis in practice is on skill and results. Training concentrates on physical fitness.

Measuring the effects of training is difficult. We need to compare people who train with people who do not. They must, however, be equally fit to start with; otherwise our results will be meaningless. We have to be certain that any changes are due to the training. Do not attempt this experiment without qualified supervision.

1 Collect a group of 'volunteers'.
2 Record the height, mass and pulse rate of each volunteer subject.
3 Measure each subject's index of fitness, by means of the Harvard Step Test (page 83).
4 Divide the group into two. Try to match the two halves for age, sex, build, fitness etc.
5 Record some other fitness measure as a check. Standing high or long jump, time to run 1 km, number of press-ups or similar will do.
6 One group does no training: this is the 'control' group.
   The others should do some kind of physical activity (running, press-ups etc.) every other day for a month: this is the 'experimental' group. Discuss the details with your supervisor.
7 After a month, repeat all the measurements with both experimental and control groups.
8 Draw up tables and graphs of the results to see whether the training has had any effect.

Other training/measurement exercises which you can try include:

shuttle-runs
pull-ups (chins)
50 m sprint
ball throwing
weightlifting (under supervision only)
squat thrusts
swimming

Hockey dribble

1 Place a series of posts or flags in a straight line at, say, 3 m intervals
2 Record the time it takes to dribble, slalom-style, along the 'course'
3 Repeat several times
4 Draw a graph showing the time for each attempt

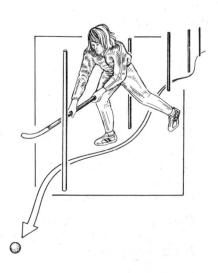

Darts

1 Set up a dart board
2 Count the number of throws needed to throw a '1'
3 Count the number needed for a '2'
4 Continue, in turn, from 3 to 20
5 Draw a graph to show the number of attempts at each number.

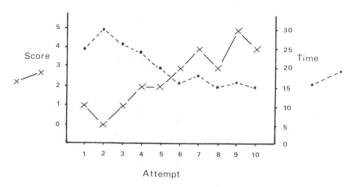

These are just three examples of the many kinds of practice measurements that can be made. Your graphs may look like the one above.

Unless the test subjects are already 'experts' at the practice task, there will be an improvement in the early stages. Then the graph levels out, as peak performance is reached. If tiredness becomes a factor, the results may even begin to get worse.

The examples are all based on the first aspect of practice: improving results, without considering technique. You could try some coaching of technique between attempts, to see whether this affects the results. If we are worried about technique, rather than results, a different approach may be helpful.

Experimentally, the difficulty is to choose a skill the subjects don't already have. One way is to try to develop a technique using the 'wrong' hand (or foot). Right-handed people should use their left hands, and vice-versa. Practice may now need to be over a much longer period before effects are noticed. And many other factors may be found to influence the results:

noise
tiredness
possession of similar skills ('transfer')
competition
understanding the mechanics of the task
not knowing the result of each attempt

Complex skills like swimming take a long time to master, but practice and coaching of actual techniques certainly help. Here, analysis of movement (Chapter 4) may give useful information. Many athletes will not appreciate how odd their technique is unless they can see it for themselves.

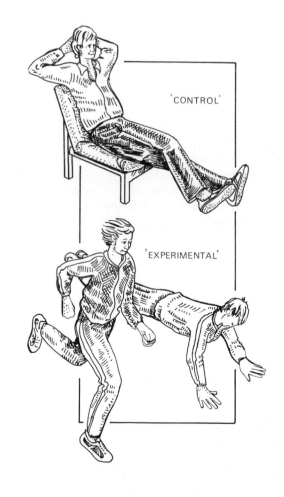

What is technology?

Just as science can satisfy our need to understand, technology meets our needs for better and more useful objects. Science produces knowledge; technology produces things.

The process is parallel to that of science:

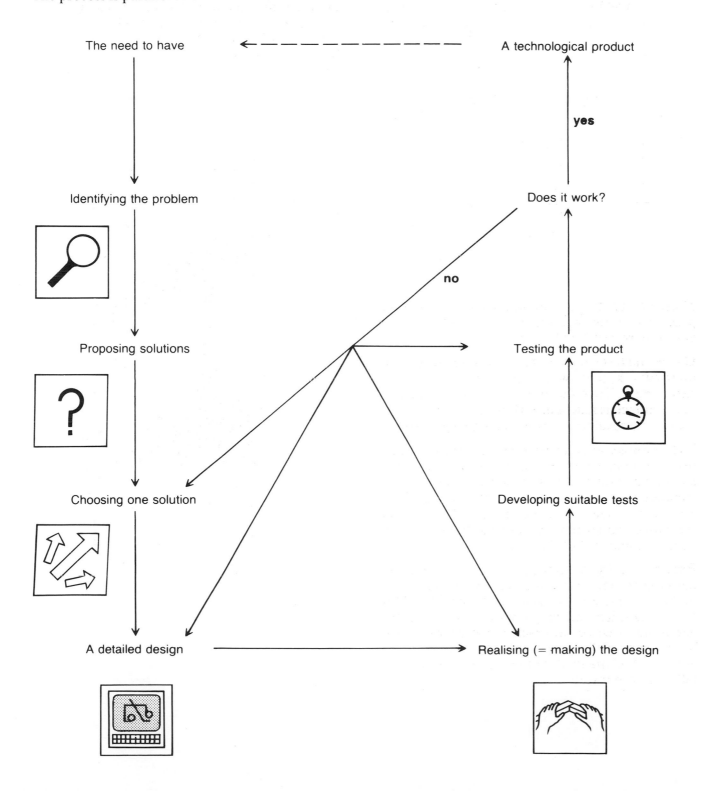

Technology on the white line

DESIGN ON THE GRAND PRIX

These are the kind of headlines which newspapers have used to announce recent advances in sports technology. Many improvements in athletic standards have been due to advances in physiology: diet, training methods, better understanding of endurance and stamina. Some have simply been due to changes in the rules: hurdlers were not originally allowed to knock over any barriers. We are more recently, however, seeing an impact of technological development. Sometimes technology is too good! The turbo-charged engine, for example. With a turbo-charger, the exhaust gas is used to force extra fresh air into the engine. This makes it more powerful – too powerful and dangerous for both drivers and spectators. So, like the javelin (page 46) the rules have been changed.

3

What to do with data

What does it mean?

Recording figures in tables is not the end of the business of data handling. We must always try to draw some conclusions; we have to *interpret* the results, to try and explain them.

Have a look at this table.

Month	Aug	Sept	Oct	Nov	Dec	Jan	Feb	Mar	Apr
Points	4	11	8	6	5	5	2	5	11

The club obviously played badly in the winter, particularly in February. Or did it? There are several other possible explanations; a few are given here:

(a)   fewer matches played (bad weather etc.);
(b)   more difficult opposition;
(c)   fewer home games;
(d)   several key players injured.

In fact, there is no information to tell us how well they played at any time, only their success in getting league points. And this can be seen more easily on a graph.

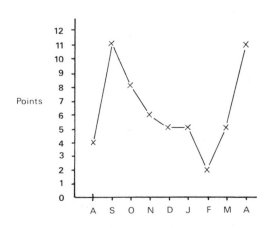

Success of a soccer club

Bar charts, histograms and graphs

Although results tables carry much useful information, data is often more easily understood if it can be shown in a more pictorial way.

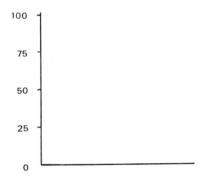

Bar charts, histograms and graphs are ways of doing this, particularly if we are interested in the relationship between two things. They all have features in common, but there are also important differences.

Each has two axes, lines at right angles, which form the limits. The vertical axis is always marked with evenly spaced numbers which often, but not always, start from 0.

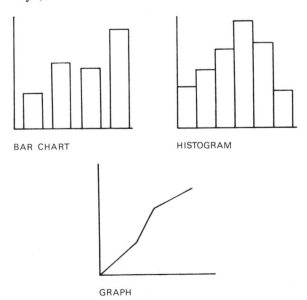

BAR CHART   HISTOGRAM

GRAPH

Bar charts

The horizontal axis of a bar chart is not usually marked with numbers, but with words. Bar charts are used to show features which are distinct from each other, such as males and females, different sports or nationalities. For this reason, there is no definite order for the bars, and spaces are often left between them.

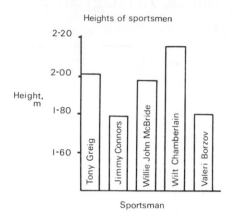

Histograms

Histograms deal with continuous, numerical data: numbers in order. Often, this data comes in groups covering a range of values.

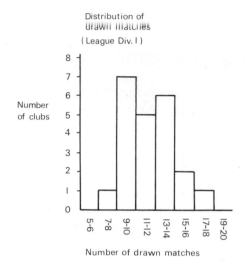

Graphs

In a graph both axes are marked with equally spaced numbers. Definite points (dots or crosses) are joined together. Graphs can be used to show any data in which both parts are sets of single numbers.

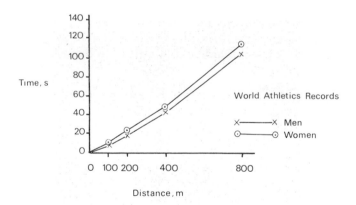

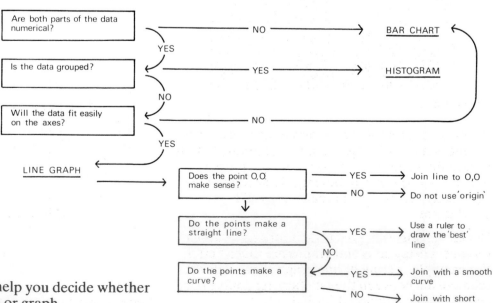

Selectagraph

You can use this figure to help you decide whether to use bar chart, histogram or graph.

Interpreting the data

Let's look at some more results and see what they tell us. The bar chart shows the numbers of sportsmen treated for brain damage at one unit in a year. What do the figures tell us?

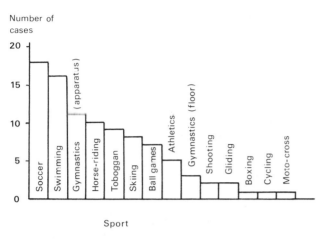

Cases of brain damage

Is boxing safe?

A first idea is that soccer is very dangerous, while boxing is relatively safe. A moment's thought tells us that this cannot be so. Far more people play soccer than compete in boxing; we need to know how many before we can reach any valid conclusions.

Bar charts normally give little information about reasons. Histograms and graphs are much better. For example, a straight line graph shows a direct relationship between the two factors: double one, and the other is doubled (or halved).

A curved graph may have one of several meanings. Often it suggests that a limit is being reached, or that a third factor is more important.

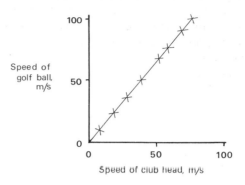

A direct relationship

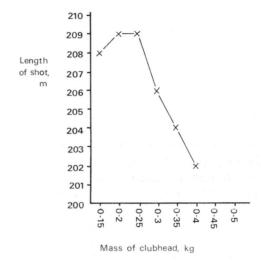

Other factors included

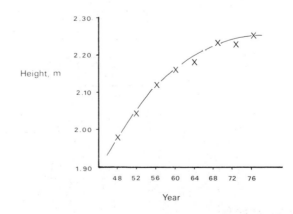

A limit approaching

Sports records

Much useful data can be obtained from sports records – the Olympic Games, Football League tables, and so on. Presented graphically, features may become clear which were not so obvious in even the best of tables.

Year	1910	1920	1930	1940	1950	1960	1970	1980
Height, m	3.9	4.2	4.3	4.5	4.6	4.8	5.3	5.6

Take, for example, the world pole vault record:

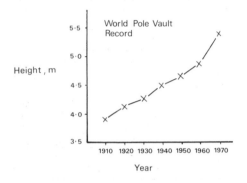

It is easy to see from the graph that something dramatic happened between 1960 and 1970. Can you suggest what this might have been?

In fact, it was the introduction of the glass fibre pole.

Pole vaulter

Poles have at various times, been made of bamboo, aluminium and glass fibre. The introduction of the glass fibre pole had a marked effect on the heights jumped. Glass fibre is an interesting material. It is known as a 'composite', made up of two different materials. Just as bones are made of a group of soft, flexible fibres in a matrix (glue) of inorganic material, so glass fibre is made of fibres of glass embedded in a plastic matrix. The resulting composite has the strength of one material, and the flexibility of the other.

The latest development uses fibres of carbon, and promises to be even better than its predecessor.

Similarly the odd results of the 1968 Mexico Olympics show up clearly if graphs are plotted of Olympic winning performances. The high altitude conditions changed the atheletes' performance abilities. Most of the graphs are similar shapes, a flattening curve, apart from occasional peculiarities caused by exceptional athletes. A change in technique or equipment may also affect the pattern. But most oddities are in the 1968 results.

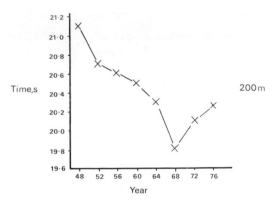

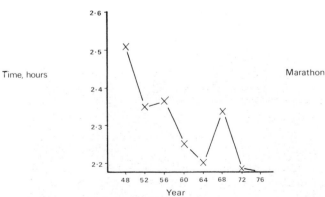

Predicting records

If the world record each year is plotted a curve is produced. This can be used to predict future records. This is done either by extending the curve (dotted line) or mathematically.

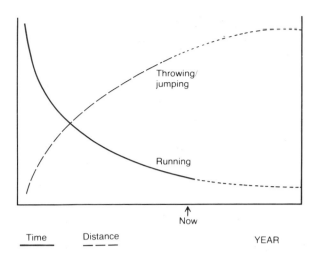

Time   Distance   YEAR

Performance differences

Here's some information showing differences between the sexes in some world records.

Event	Distance	Male	Female	% relation-ship
Swimming	100 m free	48.42	54 73	88.4
	200 m free	1:47.44	1:57.55	91.3
	400 m free	3:47.38	4:05.45	92.6
	800 m free	7:50.64	8:17.12	94.6
	1500 m free	14:54.76	15:52.10	89.4
	100 m back	54.91	1:00.59	90.6
	200 m back	1:58.14	2:08.60	91.9
	100 m breast	1:01.65	1:07.91	90.8
	200 m breast	2:13.34	2:27.27	90.5
	100 m b/fly	52.84	57.93	91.2
	Swimming, mean			91.9
Athletics	100 m	9.92	10.49	94.6
	200 m	19.72	21.34	92.4
	400 m	43.29	47.60	90.9
	800 m	1:41.73	1:53.28	89.8
	1500 m	3:29.46	3:52.47	95.4
	10 000 m	27:03.23	30:13.74	89.5
	Running, mean			92.1
	10 km walk	38:02.6	42:14.2	90.1
	High jump	2.44	2.09	85.7
	Long jump	8.90	7.52	85.5
	Overall, mean			89.7

For the world mile record, the prediction is that it will reach 3 min 46.65 s in 1998 – and then improve no further.

The equation for this is:

$$r = 4.777 - 0.02039t + 0.000104t^2$$
(where r = record and t = year – 1900)

This is used in the computer program (Appendix A, page 108) which will produce a table or a graph.

In a wide range of events, the best female performances are consistently close to 90% of the best male performances.

Roger Bannister – under 4 minutes in 1954

Steve Cram – 3 minutes 46.32 seconds in 1985

The consistency between men's and women's records is quite surprising. The range in difference is only from 85.5% (long jump) to 95.4% (1500 m). Overall, men are about 11% faster than women, regardless of distance, swimming stroke, or even when we compare running and swimming.

This kind of agreement is always worth looking for in any kind of data. We are looking for 'significance' in the figures: do they form some sort of pattern, or are they haphazard or random? In some cases, we may need a statistical test to check any apparent agreement.

For example, if a survey uses basic personal data, such as age, sex, level of fitness, you can compare the answers from different groups of people.

Sorting out the results of a survey can be as hard as asking the right questions. For example, what does this tell you?

	Boys	Girls
Play tennis	22	27
Do not	28	23

Can we say that more children do not play tennis (51) than do (49)? Or were we just lucky with our sample? If the next three people asked were players, this might suggest the opposite. Similarly, can we state that more girls really do play tennis? Could this be a chance result?

The statistics needed to answer this are more than can be dealt with here. What the statistical test would tell is that the result is *not* at all significant. In this case there is no real boy/girl difference.

Logarithmic graphs

Look again at the table of world records. Try to plot a graph of the running records (100–1500 m), men's against women's. Assuming that you remember to convert all the times into seconds, the numbers range from 9 to 210, and from 10 to 232. Can you get them conveniently on to one axis?

If we include the 5000 m, 10 000 m and marathon, the task becomes impossible. The solution is to use a 'logarithmic' graph. There are three ways of doing this:

(a)   use special logarithmic graph paper;
(b)   look up logarithms in tables, and plot these instead of the original numbers;
(c)   mark the axis so that each position is ten times the value of the previous one:

Some examples of the use of logarithmic graphs are shown below. See if you can find others elsewhere in the book.

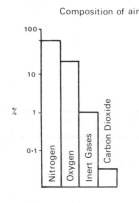

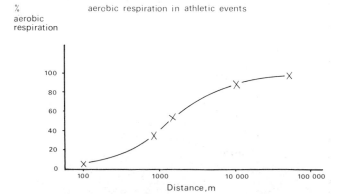

A sport science advertisement

These extracts come from a 'scientific' advertisement for the *Plus 6* golf ball.

'Many different tests have been carried out which we believe you will find completely meaningful and fair. Our new test has to be completely fair, because two balls are hit at the same time, instead of one at a time as in previous methods. This means that each hit is a true comparison – because all conditions, such as wind, rain, temperature, humidity etc., are clearly identical for each stroke.

Our test is true to life because the velocity of the club head is set within the range of human capability, and the angle of the head is 11°, that of a No. 1 wood.

Our green at the testing range is 175 m from the hitting machine; in front of the green is rough.

We fired each (of four other brands) at the same time as the *Plus 6* over a total of 100 hits. Throughout the test we alternated the *Plus 6* between the right and left tee.

The results on the chart show how many of each brand reached the green:

Comparison ball		Plus 6
Brand A	53	91
Brand B	11	94
Brand C	81	93
Brand D	28	91

These results speak for themselves.'

Do they? There are clearly some very good features in the design of the test. You might like to list these. But it is also possible to make several criticisms: can you think of any?

Would you be persuaded by this advert to use the *Plus 6* ball?

Plus 6 is manufactured by Uniroyal Ltd.

Problem page

■ Design and make devices for automatic measuring and/or recording of sport science data.

■ Devise a novel sports skill and investigate the effects of practice on its performance.

Is the skill more easily learned by those who play similar sports? By those who play any kind of sport?

■ Investigate whether swimming training wearing a weighted belt improves performance under normal conditions.

How do I measure up?

Tessa Sanderson

M. Pitman

Aurelia Dobre

William 'the Refrigerator' Perry

Most people have some idea of what their 'ideal' sportsperson would be like, in terms of build, strength, temperament and so on. Such views will be affected by thoughts of particular sports. Jockeys and basketball players need rather different body designs.

In this chapter, we will look at some of the physical factors which make up a sportsperson. We will see how they can be measured, and, with our own set of results, decide at which sports each should be best – at least, in theory.

Mass and weight

To scientists, 'mass' and 'weight' have different meanings. Mass is how much of an object (or person) there is; weight is the force with which this mass pushes down on to the Earth. Weight should be recorded in newtons because it is a measure of force; mass is measured in kilograms.

It will be useful to know your own body mass. You can find it by standing on platform scales, reading in kilograms (kg).

Make a note of your body mass. You will need to refer to it again, and you will also be able to compare yourself with top-class sportsmen and women, as well as with your friends and others of your age.

Body mass in sport

Body mass is an important factor in any sport. For some sports it is so vital that there are rules about it. For others, there may be a definite advantage in being heavy. There are even some sports, or certain parts of them, where lightness is an advantage.

swimming:
   long distance
   sprinting
table tennis

tennis
volley ball
weightlifting
wrestling

You will probably have found few sports in which body mass by itself is particlarly important, if we ignore the factor of height or general build. Only the 'combat' sports and weightlifting actually have rules about it, to prevent unfair competition and injury.

Can you estimate the body mass of each of the sports participants shown?

From the sports given, make lists of those which

(a)   have rules about body mass,
(b)   are best for heavy people,
(c)   are best for light people,
(d)   are not affected by body mass.

archery
athletics:
   distance running
   high jump
   long jump
   sprinting
   throwing
badminton
basketball
boxing
canoeing
cricket
darts
fencing
golf
gymnastics
hockey

horse riding:
   racing
   show-jumping
ice hockey
judo
netball
rowing:
   oarsman
   coxswain
rugby:
   forward
   back
skating
skiing
soccer
squash

Adrian Moorhouse

Daley Thompson

Steffi Graff

Carl Lewis

Height

Height, like mass, can be an important factor in sport. It is fairly easy to list those sports where being very tall is an advantage, and others where it is an advantage in certain positions. But, however, many short sportsmen there may be, it is difficult to think of sports where being short – as opposed to light – is a real advantage. And there are no sports which have rules about height.

Choose from the sports given before and make a list of those for which it is best to be

(a)   tall,
(b)   tall, for certain positions only,
(c)   short.

As with mass, it will be useful to know your own weight. You will need someone to help you, to make a mark on the wall or blackboard, and a metre rule or two.

Try to estimate the height of each sports personality shown.

Height and mass

The graphs below will give you some idea of how you measure up in terms of height and mass, compared with others of your age. Make sure you look at the right graph–male or female.

Are you above, below or average mass for your height?

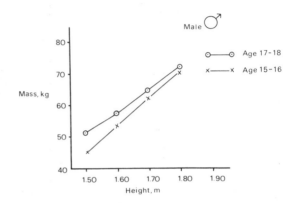

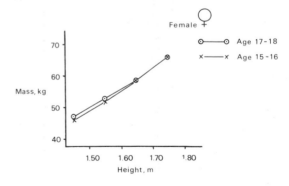

Remember that these are mean (average) values: you are not peculiar if you are not exactly average.

Surface area

Once you have measured your height and mass, it is possible to find out how large your surface area is: how much skin you have.

You could measure the surface area by wrapping the body in paper, but it is easier to use an equation or a chart.

Surface area $= (\text{mass})^{0.425} \times (\text{height})^{0.725} \times 0.00718$

(This is an empirical – trial and error – equation.)

With the equation we can calculate the surface area from the height (in cm this time) and mass (in kg).

You really need a calculator with a y^x key for this – or a computer.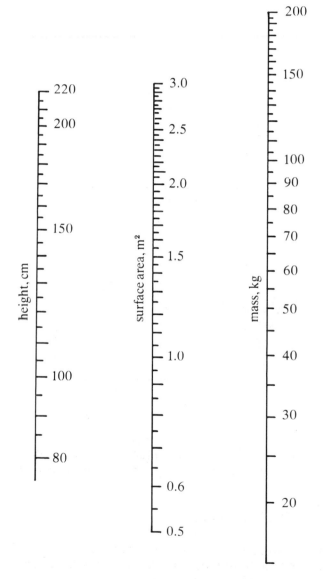

Without such a calculator, use this chart. Line up your mass and height with a ruler, and your surface area is given where it crosses the central scale.

Body shape

The technical term for body shape is *somatotype*. There are three components:

> endomorph – roundness,
> mesomorph – muscularity,
> ectomorph – linearity (tall, thin).

Each of these is rated on a scale from 1 to 7, giving a 3-figure somatotype value. Values are often plotted on a somatogram when it is found that athletes from similar sports occur in clusters.

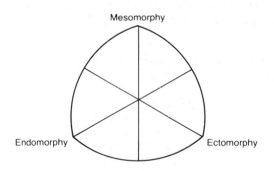

Sample values are given:

Sport	Endo-morphy	Meso-morphy	Ecto-morphy	Somato-type
Golf	4.1	4.0	2.7	443
Gymnastics	2.1	4.0	3.4	243
Swimming	3.2	4.6	2.6	353
Volleyball	4.2	3.7	3.3	443
Shot putt	5.3	5.2	1.7	552

What makes me like I am?

The simple answer to this question is 'bones, muscles and fat'.

In this last section of the chapter we shall look at this answer in a bit more detail. Firstly, those bones, with all their strange names; without them we'd be nothing but a mass of jelly on the floor. And the muscles too; their names are not much better, but without them our joints would fold up, and we'd be crunchy jelly.

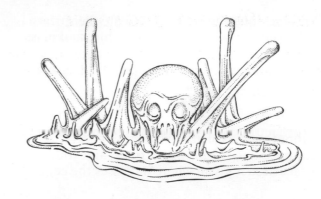

You can see the main bones and muscles – and their names – here.

Where the bones and muscles act together – in our joints – there are four other important materials:

cartilage: prevents friction between bones
synovial fluid: lubricates ('oils') the joint
tendons: join muscle to bone (non-elastic)
ligaments: join bone to bone (elastic)

Knee and hip joints are shown below.

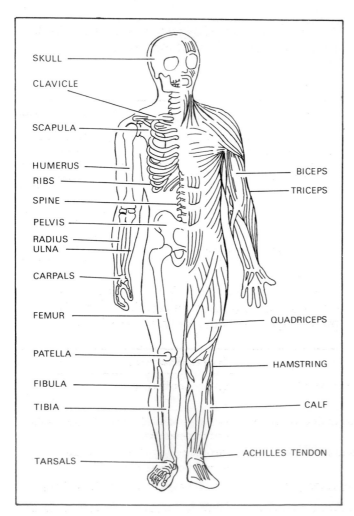

SKULL
CLAVICLE
SCAPULA
HUMERUS
RIBS
SPINE
PELVIS
RADIUS
ULNA
CARPALS
FEMUR
PATELLA
FIBULA
TIBIA
TARSALS
BICEPS
TRICEPS
QUADRICEPS
HAMSTRING
CALF
ACHILLES TENDON

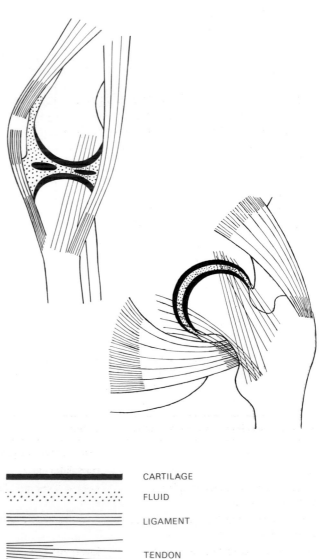

CARTILAGE
FLUID
LIGAMENT
TENDON

Sex difference and sport

Bones, muscles and fat are the same substances in males and females, but the amounts of each are not:

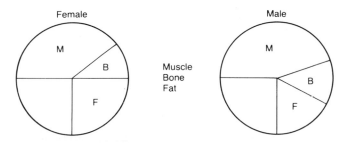

Somatotypes, too, are different. In particular, they change differently during adolescence:

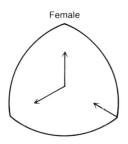
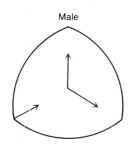

Don't forget, though, that there is great variation within each sex. The best/fastest/tallest female will be better/faster/taller than the worst/slowest/shortest male, more so even than the 'average' male.

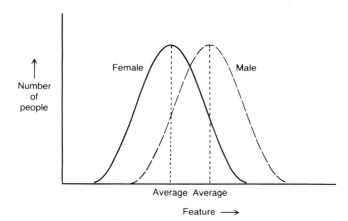

Similar curves can also be drawn for different age groups.

A factor which may affect the performance of women is menstruation. For some women athletes, success follows almost exactly the pattern of their monthly menstrual cycle. To avoid losing a gold medal because the championships are a week too early (or late), many take drugs like the 'pill' to control their cycles. Similarly, there is evidence of gymnasts artificially delaying the start of puberty. This not only postpones menstruation, but prevents the laying down of fatty tissues.

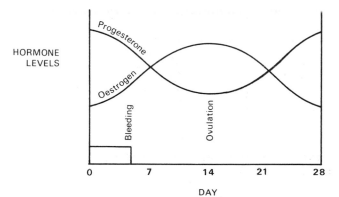

Recent studies have suggested that activity itself may postpone the start of menstruation (menarche):

Group	Age at menarche (years)
Non-athletes (control)	12.3
School/college athletes	13.0
National athletes	13.6
Olympic athletes	13.7
US Olympic volleyball team	14.2

Was it ever right to exclude women from the Olympic Games? Or from certain events? To provide special events for women? Will women

Comparison of female with male	Effect	Sports difference
smaller, shorter	lower centre of gravity; lighter frame	gymnastics: beam (f)
wider pelvis	runs differently	—
shorter limbs, narrower shoulders, different arm angle	poorer leverage of arms; throws 'round-arm'	racket games and throws: f much weaker; no f hammer throw
more endomorphic, less mesomorphic; less muscle, more fat	lower strength: mass ratio	disadvantaged in 'power' events; gymnastics: rings (m)
less blood, fewer red blood cells, less haemoglobin; and smaller heart and lungs	lower oxygen carrying capacity and uptake	(disadvantage reduced by lower body mass)

ever be as good as men? Does 9% less muscle mean 9% less performance?

The records suggest that women perform at about 90% of the men's level. But in 1956 it was nearer 85% and in 1921 75%. On this (statistical) basis it has been predicted that women will catch up. As soon as 1990 (!) in the marathon, and by 2066 in the 200 m.

Race and sport

When Jesse Owens won several gold medals in the 1936 Munich Olympic Games, Hitler was not pleased because it did not fit his ideas of the 'supreme race'. Now, in the 1990s, it seems quite normal for many of the world's leading sportsmen and women to be black. Indeed, it is thought unusual if the heavyweight boxing champion and Olympic sprint champion are not black. Certainly, in these power events, such racial difference seems to tell, yet top-class black tennis players are rarer. In distance running, however, it is the wispy, high-altitude born Kenyans and Ethiopians who have done exceptionally well in recent years.

One factor is the predominance of different somatotypes in each racial group. In the same way that male/female differences contribute to performance, these racial differences may be significant too. It is not the race itself, but the somatotype which is crucial.

Suitability for sport

We can now consider the physical factors that affect a person's choice of sport. See if you can choose the best sport (from the symbols given) for each of the sportsmen and women shown.

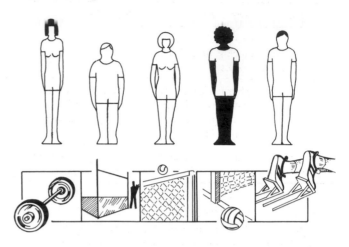

Yvonne Cawley

Pele

Jesse Owens

Which sport are you best suited for?

Looking at each feature in turn, rule out any unsuitable sports. The table gives some ideas; see if you can add any more.

Feature	Good for	Poor for
Tall	basketball, cricket, fencing, netball, rugby (forward), volleyball	
Heavy	athletics (throwing), rowing (oarsman), rugby, (forward), weight-lifting	athletics (distance running), jockey, rowing (coxswain)
High centre of gravity	athletics (jumping), diving	boxing, judo, ski-ing, weight-lifting, wrestling

The graph shows the heights of Olympic competitors at various events, plotted against mass. Notice how similar in shape the female and male curves are – they are only displaced diagonally.

How do your height and mass compare with those shown?

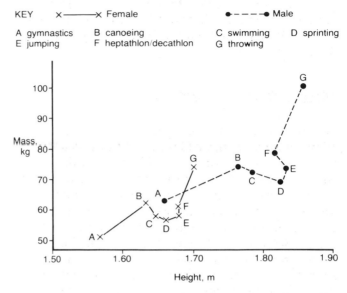

KEY   x———x Female   ●----● Male

A gymnastics   B canoeing   C swimming   D sprinting
E jumping   F heptathlon/decathlon   G throwing

Problem page

Before tackling the problems it will be useful to know something about bones.

Bones contain two types of material:

living fibres, which provide flexibility, and non-living matrix, which provide strength.

By soaking a bone in acid you can remove the matrix, leaving only the flexible fibres.

Over a hot flame you can burn away the fibres, leaving only the very brittle matrix. (Note: *very* smelly!)

bone − matrix → fibres
bone − fibres → matrix

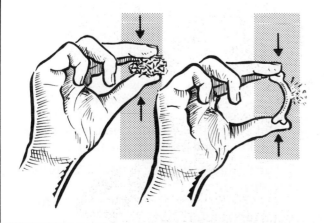

■ Design and build a system to measure the bending of a bone under stress.

(*Do **not** use a human bone!*)

■ What force is needed to break a bone?

Does it depend on the kind of force applied, e.g. sudden blow, sustained pressure?

5

Movement

Analysing movement

If we are to study any sport, we must have a way of looking closely at movements. Most movement in sport happens so quickly that the unaided eye is unable to appreciate it. This section shows a few of the ways of analysing movement, breaking it down into small units for study.

Flicker-book

Most of us have at some time drawn pin-men in the corner of the pages of a book. When flicked quickly, they give the impression of movement. You can make your own flicker-book by drawing on several pieces of paper, then stapling them together. Try your own sporting action, or copy the drawing.

You'll find it more effective if you

(a) use a simple action, and
(b) have very small stages between each drawing.

Using a flicker-book is really cheating, though. You either have to keep changing your drawings until they look 'right', or else you have to use frames from films – or someone else's drawings. Let's see how the drawings were obtained.

Film/Video-tape

Cine film is really a kind of transparent flicker-book. It is made up of thousands of separate photographs, taken at the rate of 18 or 24 per second. Looked at in quick succession they give the appearance of a continuously moving picture. Video-tape (TV film) is more continuous, but it still depends on the speed of scan.

The individual photographs ('frames') can be projected and copied, or they can be traced. For fairly slow actions, every frame is not needed. For very fast actions the camera has to run at a high speed, so that more frames are taken in the same time.

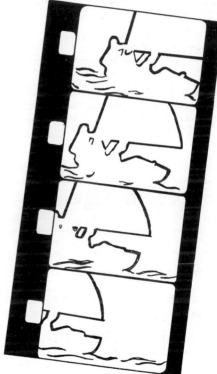

It isn't necessary, though, to make drawings. Running the projector at slower speeds, or frame by frame, is often enough for us to see how a movement is really made.

Still photographs

A film, then, is a series of still photographs taken in rapid succession. It is possible to take a set of photographs during a sporting action with an ordinary still camera – as long as the film can be wound on quickly enough. Some modern (and expensive) cameras now have a motor-driven film wind. But even with a simple camera there is a way of making such a series:

1 Set up a simple sporting action, e.g. sprint start or tennis serve.
2 Take a photograph at the start of the action.
3 Wind on the film.

4 Repeat the action; take a photograph just after the start.
5 Keep repeating the action, taking each photograph slightly later than the previous one.
6 Mount the prints as if they were from a single sequence.

For best results, the action must be identical each time, and the background must stay the same. (Otherwise people may appear and disappear in what is supposed to be a fraction of a second!)

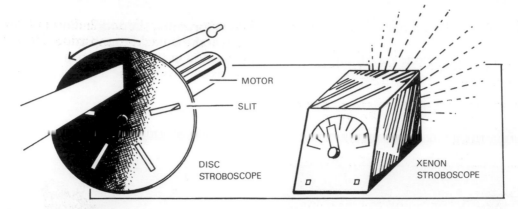

MOTOR

SLIT

DISC
STROBOSCOPE

XENON
STROBOSCOPE

Stroboscope

The stroboscope has long been a scientific tool. Now it is increasingly common in entertainment ('disco' lighting) and car maintenance ('timing' light). There are two types of stroboscope:

(a) a regularly flashing light, usually xenon filled, which can be set to flash at any speed;

(b) a rotating disc, with regular slits, in front of a bright light.

When the light flashes on, any object in its path can be seen. When it is off, nothing is visible.

Any continuous movement will be seen at intervals. A ball in flight will appear, disappear, appear again. . . . Legs will seem to jerk. A bouncing ball may seem never to move at all.

The exact effect depends on how the speed of flashing compares with the speed of movement. For a regularly repeating action – running on the spot, squat thrusts etc. – the movement will appear as in the table:

Speed of flash (relative to action)	Type of movement
very much faster	normal
slightly faster	slow motion
exactly the same	stationary
slightly slower	slow backwards!
very much slower	jerky

A camera with its shutter held open will record only the positions when the light flashes on, like in the judo sequence below.

Muscles and movement

By using any – or all – of these techniques we can record and analyse movement. Any kind of movement: jumping; running; swimming; gymnastics; the flight of balls, shuttlecocks, javelins and disci; and many others. What sports have in common is the movement of human muscle.

The main muscles of the body were shown on page 28. One of their important features is that they work in pairs. Muscles can only do work when they contract, when they shorten. To move a joint therefore needs two muscles; one to straighten, one to bend. The best known of these *antagonistic* pairs is the biceps and triceps of the upper arm.

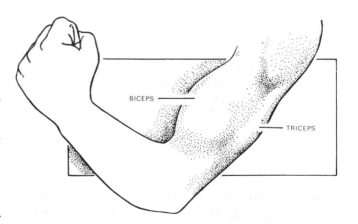

BICEPS

TRICEPS

Levers

Muscles which bend joints are *flexors*. Those which straighten joints are *extensors*.

Joint	Flexor	Extensor
elbow	biceps	triceps
knee	hamstrings	quadriceps

1st order levers are the most efficient because

(a)   the effort is working with gravity;
(b)   the effort/pivot distance may be large.

They are rare in human limbs, but an example is found in the ankle.

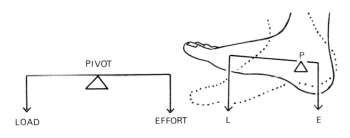

Carrying a vaulting pole is a sporting example of a 1st order lever.

2nd order levers may also have a large effort/pivot distance, but the effort here is working against gravity. Standing on tiptoe provides an example in the body.

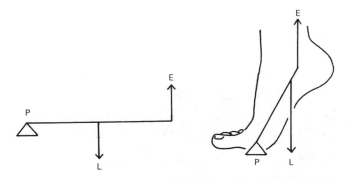

The sailor is relying on a 2nd order lever to prevent the boat from capsizing. Here the effort is the tension in the rope.

3rd order levers are the least efficient, but the most common in the body. The effort/pivot distance is small and the effort works against gravity. Lifting the forearm is an example, as are all types of throw.

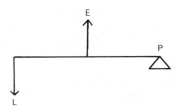

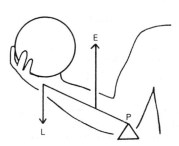

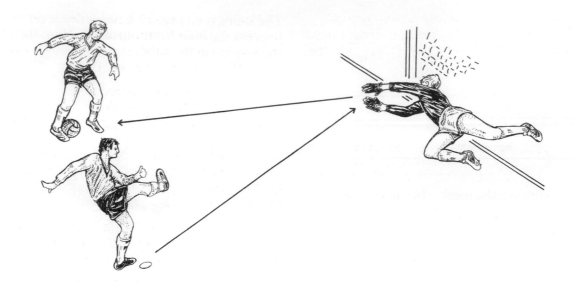

Newton's laws of motion

Isaac Newton is perhaps best known for his work on light and gravity. He would, however, have understood much of the science involved in sport – even though he never played himself. Most important are his three laws of motion.

Consider a football on the penalty spot. A player kicks it towards the goal. The goalkeeper throws himself at it. The ball rebounds to a defender. He stops it.

Newton's first law is in action above. An object at rest stays at rest (ball on spot) until a force acts on it (kicked). Once moving, an object travels in a straight line (towards goal) until a force acts on it (goalkeeper). It then moves in a straight line again (rebound) until a further force brings it to rest (defender).

Would you rather be hit by a golf ball or a table-tennis ball? For the same strength of throw (the same force), a light ball accelerates faster than a heavy ball. But if they accelerate at the same rate, the heavy ball arrives with greater force.

In Newton's terms: acceleration = force ÷ mass
force = mass × acceleration

For example, a golf ball is 20 times heavier than a table-tennis ball, so falls with 20 times the force. (1 newton is the force which accelerates 1 kg mass at $1 \, \text{m s}^{-2}$.)

Have you ever watched a young child throw a ball? Often, he or she falls over backwards. It is easy to see that the child applies a force to the ball. Newton called this the *action*. But the ball applies an opposite force to the child. This is the *reaction*. Every force has an opposing, but equal, force.

In the diagram, the forces are in action/reaction pairs:

bodyweight (W)/contact force (N)
thrust (T)/friction (F)

Momentum

Would you rather be hit on the head by a hockey ball or a table-tennis ball?

Would you rather be hit by a tennis ball lobbed gently at $5 \, \text{m s}^{-1}$, or one served at over $50 \, \text{m s}^{-1}$?

Why?

But why does it hurt less?

Scientists have a useful concept which they call *momentum*. Momentum is a product of the mass and velocity (speed) of an object. To get its value, you simply multiply them together:

momentum = mass × velocity

So, in the examples given above:

Ball	Mass, kg	Velocity, m/s	Momentum kg.m/s
Hockey	0.16	20	3.2
T-tennis	0.0024	20	0.048
Tennis	0.067	5	0.3
Tennis	0.067	50	3

We have already seen, in Newton's 2nd law of motion, that

force = mass × acceleration.

And, as

acceleration = velocity ÷ time,

All the quantities relate together. We find that

force = momentum ÷ time.

This means that the force of impact when a ball hits something will depend on the momentum it has, and the time of contact. For a soft ball (or a soft surface), the contact time will be longer; the force will therefore be smaller.

It's not just balls which have momentum. People do, too. Provided, of course, that they are moving. There is an often controversial situation in rugby of the 'momentum' try.

'His own momentum carried him over the line,' says the commentator, or the referee, as a try is awarded. The laws of the game state that a try shall be scored 'if the momentum of a player, when held in possession of the ball, carries him into his opponents' in-goal and he first there ground the ball, even though it touched the ground in the field of play.'

As long as the player continues to move, the try is allowed. The actual amount of momentum depends on the mass of the players, since

momentum = mass × velocity.

How much faster must a 60 kg scrum-half run than a 90 kg prop-forward to have the same momentum?

If the player stops, even for a moment, he has no momentum since his velocity will then be 0, and

mass × 0 = 0

This is why a momentum try requires continuous movement.

Momentum can be passed on, from one ball to another, or from one player to another. A simple rule applies here too. The total amount of momentum is the same, before and after any collision.

Momentum comes before an impact

Energy

Motion or movement needs energy. Movement itself is a kind of energy, called motion or kinetic energy. Every moving object has some of its energy in this form.

Kinetic energy is related to momentum. It is calculated by:

$$k.e. = \frac{1}{2} \times \frac{mass \times velocity^2}{2}$$

or

$$k.e. = \frac{1}{2} \times momentum \times velocity$$

But there are other kinds of energy. The table lists them, and gives a sporting example of each:

Type of Energy	Example
Kinetic	movement of ball
Chemical	food, fuel
Heat	warming-up
Light	floodlights
Sound	bat on ball
Electricity	electric scoreboard
Potential (gravity)	high jump bar
Nuclear (atomic)	not in sport (yet!)

The cartoon strip shows a golfer's activities from eating breakfast in the morning to the applause of the crowd at the end of the day. Can you identify the different kinds of energy involved?

Centre of mass

Centre of mass can be thought of as the point at which the force of gravity acts on a body – human or object. It's where the weight is reckoned to be concentrated. For a regular, symmetrical object, such as a ball, the centre of mass is its actual centre. For irregular things like human beings, shuttlecocks and tennis rackets its position may not be so obvious.

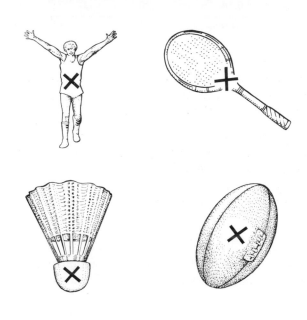

To find the centre of mass of a simple object, such as a piece of card, is fairly easy:

1 hang it from a single pivot – a pin through it,
2 hang a 'plumbline' from the same pivot,
3 mark this vertical line on the card,
4 repeat 1–3 using a different position.

Both lines will pass through the centre of mass; it is where they cross.

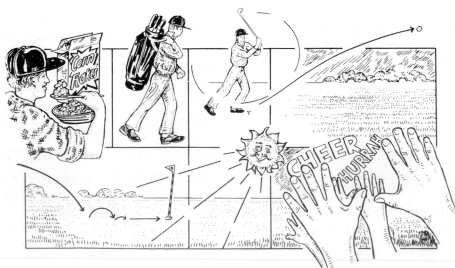

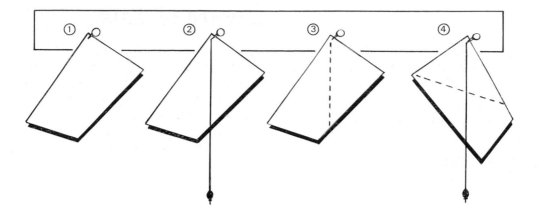

This method will work for solid objects, as long as they are not totally irregular. Be warned, though, that the centre of mass of an object can lie in space, and not in the object at all!

To find the centre of mass of a person we don't hang him from a pin, but lie him on a plank. Four measurements are needed to find the height of the centre of mass from the feet; we assume that it is otherwise exactly in the centre.

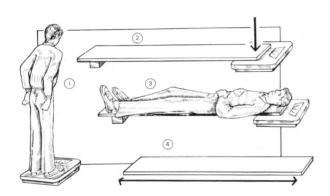

Measure:

1   the weight of the person alone – this is found by standing on platform scales marked in newtons (N);
2   the force of the plank, supported on a brick and the newton-meter scales (K);
3   the force exerted by the person lying on the plank, feet over the brick (P);
4   the length of the plank, in metres (L).

The distance of the centre of mass above a person's feet is:

$$L\frac{(P-K)}{N}$$

This gives the distance (in metres) above the feet of the body's centre of mass. It is normally a little above the navel.

The position of the centre of mass is important in two ways. One is balance.

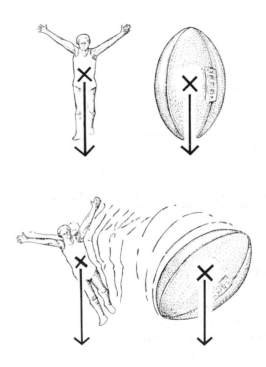

Anything, a person included, will balance if its centre of mass is directly above its base; the force of gravity will act directly down so than the weight is fully on the base.

As soon as the centre of mass moves away from its stable position above the base, the force of gravity will act more on one side than the other. The object will turn, and fall: it has become unstable.

The lower the centre of mass, the more likely it is to stay above the base; and the larger the base, the more stable the object. This means that short, round people tend to be more stable (physically, not emotionally) than tall, thin people.

One problem is that the fluid keeps moving for a while after the head has stopped. The eyes and ears are then sending different information to the brain. The result is feeling giddy or dizzy.

In any sport where keeping upright is important, a low centre of mass is an advantage.

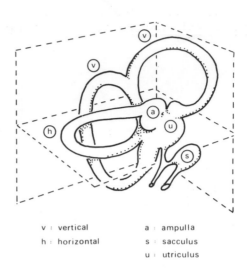

v : vertical   a : ampulla
h : horizontal   s : sacculus
                    u : utriculus

The semi-circular canals: organs of balance

Balance

Balance isn't just passive in humans, though. We can move our bodies to alter the location of the centre of mass – guided by our organs of balance.

The organs of balance (the semi-circular canals) lie within the inner ear. The three canals are set at right-angles to each other. This means that they can respond to movement in any direction.

Sense organs in each canal are sensitive to the movements of the fluid inside. Without this system we wouldn't be able to position the body correctly while swimming, diving or even walking in the dark. (In the light we rely greatly on vision for balance.)

High jump

The second feature of the position of centre of mass is its effect on work, energy and power. As we shall see later the amount of energy required for an activity depends, among other things, on how far the force is applied: twice as much energy is needed to jump 2 m as 1 m. But the distance we should really measure is the movement of the centre of mass, for it is here that the force acts.

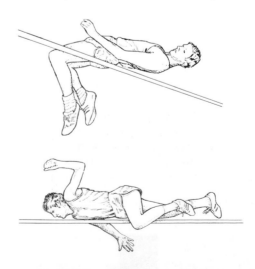

In comparing high jumps, for example, we should measure the height moved by the centre of mass of the jumper, not his feet. Look at the drawings of different high jump styles.

You should be able to see which moves the centre of mass the most, and which the least, in jumping the 'same height'. Dick Fosbury invented the 'Fosbury flop' technique as a way of gaining extra height without doing extra work.

Indeed, it is possible for the centre of mass to actually pass under the bar in both high jump and pole vault.

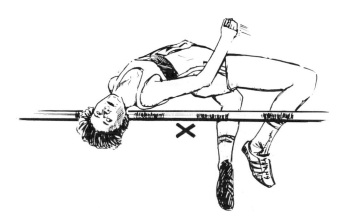

There are three factors to consider in high-jumping.

(a) raising the centre of mass as far as possible (H2);
(b) keeping the centre of mass as near the bar as possible (H3);
(c) clearing the bar with the trailing limbs.

We have seen how different techniques affect factor (b). You can see how the centre of mass ideally moves in a parabola. It also gives some idea of the importance of a high jumper having a high centre of mass (i.e. being tall and thin), and of clearing the bar by as little as possible. What height of jump would be given to the jumper whose centre of mass was raised by only 0.74 m?

Most important in the actual jump is the vertical speed at take-off. This depends on the force exerted on the ground, and the time for which the force is applied. As with the impact force on a ball, there is a direct relationship; greatest speed is given by the largest force acting for the longest time.

But, even before the athlete leaves the gound, the 'lay-out' style for clearing the bar is already developing. The upward motion is converted into a suitable body position, before the high point is reached, and the downward path begins.

Long jump

The long jump can be divided into four stages:

(a) approach   (b) take-off,
(c) flight,   (d) landing.

Identify these stages in the drawing.

HEIGHT OF JUMP = H1 + H2 − H3

Approach

The faster the forward speed 'off the board', the longer the jump. So an athlete should really give himself enough length of run to reach top speed. But this 50 m or so is too far for accuracy, so 20 or 30 m is more common, to ensure hitting the board.

Take-off

The second important factor is the upward speed at take-off, in a line from the thrusting foot through the centre of mass.

Flight

Immediately after take-off the body starts to roll forwards; any technique which turns the body against this should give a longer jump. The three flight styles (sail, hang and hitch-kick) are shown. As might be expected, the sail is easiest, but least effective; the hitch-kick the hardest to perfect, but the most efficient in increasing the length of jump.

Sail

Hang

Hitchkick

Landing

Whatever the style, the landing is made in a position with the head and feet thrown forward, the body arched, arms thrown in front. At the actual point of landing, some forward rotation is needed to stop the jumper falling backwards, as it is the rear-most mark which is measured. Ancient Greek long jumpers carried weights to correct the rotation of the body. This is not allowed in modern athletics.

Hurdling

Watch a beginner hurdle, and you see two actions: running and jumping. Watch an expert, and you see a continuous, flowing movement. Ideally, the centre of mass should rise only a little above the hurdle, in a smooth curve:

Important features of good hurdling are:

(a)   centre of mass rises little; the high point is near the hurdle;
(b)   the shorter time and longer distance spent off the ground, the better; this gives maximum speed;
(c)   wide separation of the legs, with fast backward and downward leg movements;
(d)   no pause on landing.

Sprinting

The start is more important in short races, as there is less time to make up any lost ground. Sprint starts, as we know them, were invented by fairground gamesters. They would boast that they could beat any opponent. So confident were they, that they offered to start from a 'supine' position, lying on their backs. Try it for yourself:

1   Lie on the ground, face up.
2   Roll over onto your front.
3   Push yourself up on hands and feet as if to run.
4   You will find yourself in the sprint start position.
5   Compare starting like this with starting in a perfectly upright position, either against someone else, or by timing a short distance run.

The value of the sprint start is that it gives maximum forward thrust, and the lower running position offers less air resistance. More thrust and less drag means more speed.

The manikin here may be useful in helping to understand what happens.

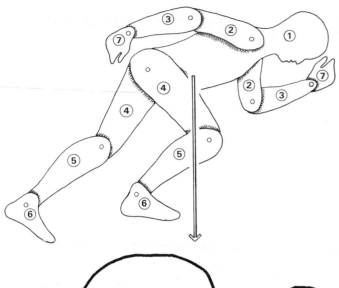

In the sprint start position shown on the left, a vertical line through the centre of mass falls in front of the feet. The runner will therefore tend to fall forwards, but the thrust applied to the ground will balance. By moving the manikin into any sporting position (by comparison with a photograph) it is possible to find out what effect the position of the centre of mass is likely to have.

Making a manikin

It is possible to measure much more about the body and to calculate more still. Head, trunk and limbs can be measured directly. Centre of mass can be found for individual body parts. Even the masses of limbs can be estimated, as their proportions are fairly standard.

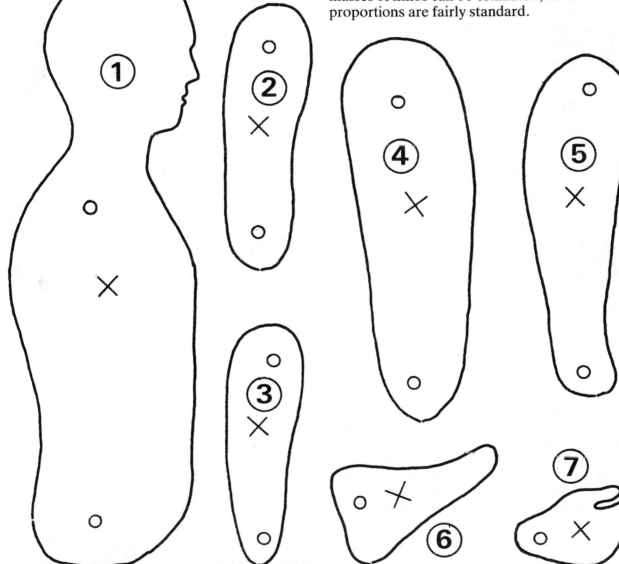

✕ **CENTRE OF MASS**

O **PIVOT POINT**

With enough information we can make a 'manikin' out of card and paper fasteners, which will be a fairly accurate model of the body. The shapes drawn on page 43 will save you a lot of trouble in measuring and calculating, although they are really for the 'standard' male 76 kg, 1.78 m athlete. They are drawn to 1/6 scale. Simply trace them onto card or photocopy them.

Lindford Christie

If you've ever tried running with your arms folded (or even behind your back!) you'll realise that arm movements are also important. The reason for the rapid arm movements of a sprinter is to balance out the body twist caused by the powerful leg action. At slower speeds there is time for the trunk to absorb this twist, so energy can be conserved by less use of the arms. Murray Halberg won the Olympic 5000 m in 1960 despite having a withered arm by leading early to avoid a sprint finish.

Close inspection of the drawing suggests that running can be divided into two stages:

(a)   drive, when the foot is in contact with the ground, and
(b)   recovery, when the leg swings forward.

Distance running

The problems of the middle- and long-distance runner are rather different from those of the sprinter. Here, the emphasis is on stamina rather than power, on economy rather than strength.

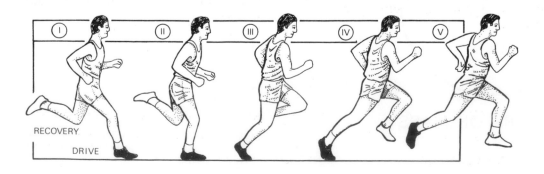

RECOVERY

DRIVE

Drive
The foot lands, on the outside first (i), then takes the full weight of the body (ii). The knee 'gives' to avoid damage (iii), and, as the foot pushes backwards, the body moves forward (iv) and takes off (v).

Recovery
As soon as the toes leave the ground (iv), the leg is bent at the hip, knee and ankle (v). It swings forward at about twice the speed of the body (i). The recovery leg is highest just as the front foot lands (ii).

Swimming also consists of alternate drive and recovery phases:

Throwing

The four throwing events – discus, hammer, javelin and shot – have certain features in common.

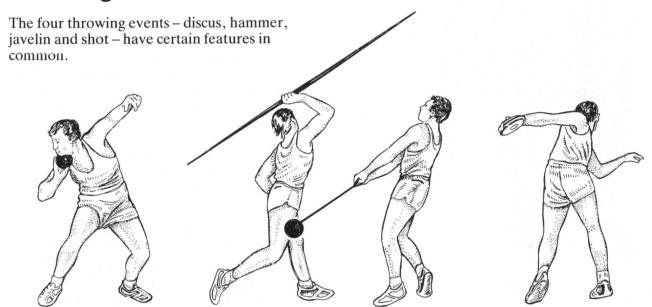

Indeed, the same scientific principles apply to the flight of any missile or projectile, object, ball or human.

In the best throws, the largest possible force is exerted for the longest possible time, in the direction of the throw. All the various aspects of a throwing technique are designed with this in mind. The outcome is a high speed of release, at the most effective angle.

The ideal angle of projection should, in theory at least, be 45°. But, while this might be so for projection from the ground, it does not apply to objects which are thrown from 2 m or so above the ground. The angle of throw for maximum distance is reduced by this factor. Its actual value depends on the exact height of throw, and the speed of release, but it is about 40° for shot putt, about 30° for javelin.

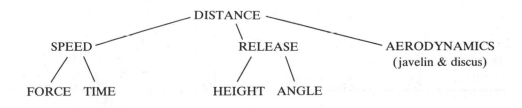

EQUAL ANGLES

Why? Because the modern, aerodynamic javelin was becoming too dangerous. With the world record at over 100 m it was in danger of being thrown into the crowd or even out of the stadium!

Mick Hill:
a sport scientist

The amount of lift on a flying discus or javelin depends on:

(a)   its shape, which affects air flow;
(b)   its angle of attack: the larger the better;
(c)   its surface area: the larger the better;
(d)   its speed: the faster the better;
(e)   the air itself – dense air gives more lift.

Of all these, the speed of release appears to be the most important.

Discus

Direction of flight

Angle of incidence

Angle of attack

Wind

Javelin

Lift

Direction of flight

Drag

Wind

The 'new' javelin was introduced to be less efficient! Changing the shape of the javelin affects its flight. Moving the centre of mass also affects it: the nearer the centre of mass is to the tip, the more the angle of attack is reduced.

DAILY SPORT OLYMPICS FOR LONDON JAVELIN THROWN FROM GATESHEAD!

Projectiles

For an object launched at a speed of u m s^{-1} at an angle of a degrees, the distance travelled is given by:

$$r = u^2 \sin 2a/g$$

(Where g $= 9.81$ m s^{-2}: acceleration due to gravity.)

N.B. Sin $2a$ is largest ($=1.0$) when $a = 45°$, so $45°$ is the optimum (best) angle.

However, this only applies if the object takes off from the ground, e.g. a golf ball. For events such as shot putt or javelin the height of release is also a factor. (For high jump and long jump we should really consider the height of the centre of mass at take-off.) The computer program (9 in Appendix A, page 108) enables any number of values to be tried.

Using this we can investigate the effect of each factor. Some idea of the release speeds and angles for a number of sports is shown.

24 m s^{-1}

30 m s^{-1}

6 m s^{-1}

38 m s^{-1}

8 m s^{-1}

Bob Beamon's amazing 1968 long jump (8.90 m) would need a take-off speed of 10 m s^{-1} at an angle of over 30°.

Bob Beamon

Left and right hand

Three observations lead us to investigate the question of using the right or left hand in sport:

(a) more top-class tennis players are left-handed than would be expected (compared with the proportion of left-handers in the whole population);
(b) many left-arm bowlers (cricket) bat right-handed, but so do most right-arm bowlers;
(c) right-handed batsmen may be coached using the left hand only, never the right hand only.

What is the significance of these observations? Do we use the term 'left' and 'right' accurately?

Look at the tennis and cricket strokes shown. The arrangement of the hands is the same in each case. The tennis player is *left*-handed, playing the sort of backhand shot favoured by such players. The cricketer is batting *right*-handed, playing a normal stroke. How can one be right-handed and the other left-handed?

Part of the difficulty is historical. For many years, left-handed people were thought to be 'odd'. Children were encouraged to write (and, presumably, to hit and throw) with the right hand. Some sports still reflect this: hockey players are forced to hold the stick in the right-handed style. Using a left-handed style and hitting with the back of the stick are forbidden.

If we look closely at a cricketer batting, we find that the top hand is used for power, the lower hand for guidance. We could argue that the 'left-hander' in fact bats right-handed, since it is the right hand on top which does most of the work. This is why single handed coaching concentrates on the 'wrong' hand.

A reason often put forward for the high proportion of left-handed tennis players is that being left-handed is a definite advantage. Because there are fewer of them opponents are not so used to dealing with them. Shots which a right-hander could not possibly get are fairly easy for a left-hander. Left-handers therefore win more games at first, and are more likely to reach club, county and national standard.

Analysing games

As well as analysing individual movements, it is often useful to do a sort of 'time-and-motion' study of a sportsman or of a match. This will give information about particular strengths and weaknesses, or about the performance of an individual team member. Here are two examples; they can easily be adapted to suit any sport.

1 Make an outline plan of a soccer pitch.
2 During a match, mark the movements of a player in a five-minute period. You can use different symbols to show walking, running, playing the ball.
3 Compare the same player at different times, or different players at the same time.

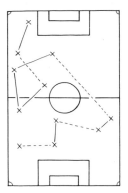

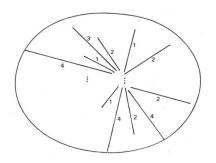

You can use this method to discover whether there is any truth in such commentators' statements as 'covered every blade of grass' and 'midfield players have a much higher work-rate'.

The second example concerns individual technique.

1   Draw an outline of a cricket field.
2   Each time the batsman plays a scoring shot, mark the direction and distance of the shot and the number of runs.
3   Use the results to compare scoring in front of and behind the wicket, leg- and off-side shots.

Problem page

■ 'It is not the speed of the runners that matters in a relay; it is the speed of the baton.'

Devise a way of measuring the speed of the baton and test the truth of the statement.

■ A diver preparing for a static dive must be perfectly balanced. Use a manikin figure to explore possible positions.

■ The carrying of weights by long-jumpers was normal practice in Ancient Greece. Find out whether this makes any difference to the length of jump. If it does, suggest the sort of weight a world-class jumper would carry: could the world record ever be 10 metres?

■ Investigate practically the effect of different approach speeds and take-off angles on long-jump performance.

How do your findings compare with the theory (see page 47)?

■ While swimming, what proportion of the time does each arm spend in

(a)   drive;
(b)   recovery?

Does it differ much in front/back crawl, breaststroke, butterfly?

When swimming faster, does this proportion change?

(Compare this with heart-beat, (page 72, Chapter 8) when the recovery, or *diastole*, becomes faster while the drive, or *systole*, stays the same.)

■ Use stroboscopic photography to analyse the flight of a shuttlecock. Is there a difference between nylon and feathered types?

At what stage of the flight does the shuttle 'flip over'?

■ Design and make a device to trigger a camera or a flash-gun at the precise moment of action.

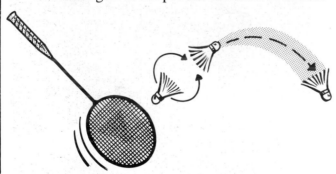

■ Analyse the entry for the Wimbledon tennis championships (or similar event) to find the proportion of left-handed players.

Is it the same for men as for women?

How does it compare with the proportion in your class, school or local tennis club?

■ Use a ticker-timer and/or electronic timing device to investigate the sprint start. Devise a means of measuring the forces applied to the ground/starting blocks – how do these forces relate to the *escape velocity*?

6

Ball games

The variety of balls

The same basic scientific principles apply to all balls, but, we need to remember that there are a lot of differences in how balls are made. As well as size and mass, how a ball behaves is affected by exactly what it is made from, whether it is hollow or solid, and what kind of surface it has.

Simple data on size and mass of common balls is given.

Ball	mass, g	diameter, cm
Cricket	160	6.4
Golf	46	4.1
Hockey	160	6.4
Rugby	410	19, 24
Soccer	420	22
Squash	24	4
Table-tennis	2.4	3.8
Tennis	57	6.4

Bounce

One of the most important features of a ball is its amount of bounce. Each game requires a certain type of bounce. Imagine a football with the bounce of a golf ball, or playing table-tennis with a squash ball!

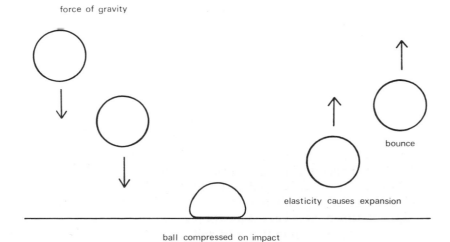

force of gravity

bounce

elasticity causes expansion

ball compressed on impact

When a ball meets a surface, something has to 'give'. This may be the ball, the surface, or both. Usually, the ball is flattened to some extent, as shown in the photograph. The fact that the ball is 'elastic' means that it can store energy for a short time, and then release it as it springs back to its original shape.

The bounciness of a ball is known by scientists as its *coefficient of restitution*. Some idea of its value for a particular ball can be found quite simply.

1 Clamp a metre rule vertically.
2 Hold a ball with its bottom at the 1 metre mark.
3 Drop it.
4 Notice the height to which it bounces – look at the bottom of the ball again.
5 Repeat for other heights.
6 Draw a graph like this.

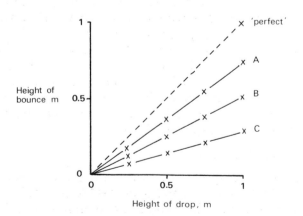

A ball never bounces as high as it falls. This is because some of the energy used in squashing the ball is lost. This energy is converted into heat. For one bounce, it is a very small amount, but for repeated bounces it may become quite noticeable. In squash, this heat is very important as the hot ball bounces better than the cold ball. (See page

60 for more information.) Some of the energy may also be lost in squashing the ground. Some ball games have rules about the bounce of a ball. For example, a basketball dropped from 2 m on to a hard floor must rebound to between 1.2 and 1.4 m.

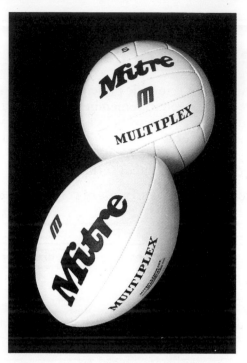

The coefficient of restitution (e) is given by

$$e = \sqrt{\text{bounce height/drop height}}$$

Values for common balls – dropped onto a wooden floor – are listed. (See page 102 for other surfaces.)

Ball	e
'Superball'	0.89
Golf	0.80
Basketball	0.76
Soccer	0.76
Volleyball	0.74
Tennis (old)	0.71
Tennis (new)	0.67
Lacrosse	0.62
Squash	0.60
Hockey	0.50
Softball	0.32
Cricket	0.31

Friction

Friction is the force which opposes the movement of any two surfaces in contact. When a ball moves across a surface, there is bound to be friction between them. The amount of friction is greatest when the ball is sliding or skidding. It is least when the ball is rolling perfectly. Then, the speed of rotation is exactly the same as the speed of forward movement. If a resting ball is hit or kicked, it first skids, then begins to roll as it picks up speed.

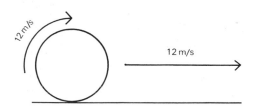

By deliberately spinning the ball as it is hit, this skidding can be reduced, or even totally removed. This is normal practice in snooker and football.

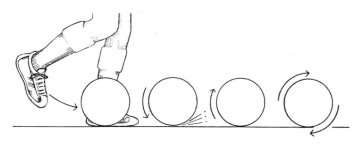

The frictional states of different balls can be compared by simple experiment.

1 Support a plank on a jack and a block so that it is perfectly level.
2 Put the ball on the plank at the jack end.
3 Carefully raise the jack until the ball rolls.
4 Measure the number of turns on the jack and/or the angle of the plank.
5 Repeat the measurements for other balls.

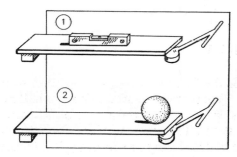

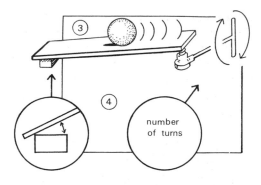

'Hitters'

It's strange how different words are used for the various hitters we use in ball games. Make sure you know which is which by matching these up:

BAT	badminton	billiards
CLUB		cricket
CUE	croquet	golf hockey
MALLET		snooker
RACKET	squash	tennis
STICK		table-tennis

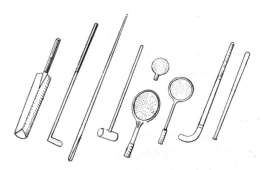

Each type of hitter has its own features, but they all have one thing in common in the way they are used. Each is actually in contact with the ball for a very short period of time. The time of an actual hit is only a tiny fraction of a second. For a golf drive it may be only 0.0005 s; in tennis, perhaps 0.005 s. This very short contact time means that enormous forces have to be used to move the balls at their normal playing speeds, since

force = mass × velocity ÷ time.

To get a ball speed of 70 m s^{-1}, the forces needed are 800 N in tennis, and over 6000 N in golf. This is equivalent to the weight of a small family car!

	Golf	Tennis
Ball mass, kg	0.046	0.057
Impact time, s	0.0005	0.005
Force, N	6440	798

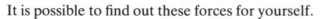

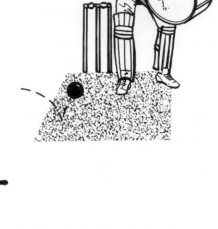

It is possible to find out these forces for yourself.

1 Wrap a ball in aluminium foil, then find its mass.
2 Fix a piece of foil to the face of a bat or racket.
3 Connect wires from the foil on bat and ball to a timer. Wire it up so that the timer starts when contact is made, and stops when contact is broken.
4 Use a stop-watch (or photocell timing system) to time the flight of the ball across the room, and also measure the distance covered.
5 Hit the ball; record the data.

Work out the hitting force like this:

$$\text{force (N)} = \frac{\text{mass (kg)} \times \text{velocity (m s}^{-1})}{\text{contact time (s)}}$$

and

$$\text{velocity (m s}^{-1}) = \frac{\text{flight time (s)}}{\text{distance (m)}}$$

The answer will be in newtons. Compare your figures with the examples given. Try it for different balls and hitters.

Centre of percussion

The material used to make a hitter will affect the flight of the ball it hits. The small dents in a cricket bat tell us that energy is lost as the ball is hit. The strings of a tennis racket are very elastic, so little energy is lost. A racket with two sets of strings (*double strung*) has been banned because it is too elastic. Friction between ball and hitter may also be important; this is why the snooker player chalks the tip of his cue.

The effectiveness of a hit also depends on where the ball strikes bat or racket. The best point is the *centre of percussion*.

Investigation

A simple investigation will demonstrate this.

1 Attach a length of dowel or metal rod at right angles to the handle of a racket or bat.
2 Suspend it from two horizontal supports.
3 Hit it with a hand-held ball at various points. Does it swing or jump?

Position of hit	Effect
above c of p	racket swings back
at c of p	racket jumps away
below c of p	racket swings forward

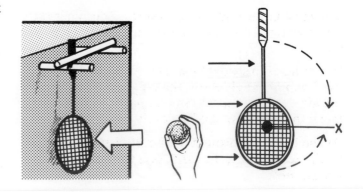

Explanation:

Imagine the racket pivoted at the centre of percussion.

Hitting above or below will make it spin, using up some of the energy.

Hitting exactly at the pivot produces no spin: all the energy is available.

Surfaces

Why is the surface of each ball different?

The material of which a ball is made affects its surface. Leather panels used to make soccer balls can't be stitched to give the smooth surface of a squash or table-tennis ball. The way in which the ball is made can, however, have an effect. Machine-made cricket balls have an artificial 'seam' added to give some of the effects of the traditional, hand-made type.

The most important factor in surface design is the effect which the surface has on the flight of the ball.

It is difficult to study the moving ball, so scientists use a wind-tunnel. Here, the ball stays still, and the air is moved past it. Smoke particles in the air mean that the flow can be clearly seen.

As the ball flies through the air, it disturbs the flow of air. Sometimes, the flow stays smooth, or *streamlined*:

high energy air at low pressure

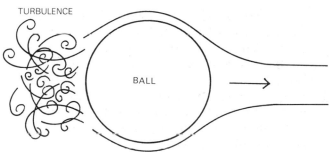

But, when friction between air and ball increases, the flow becomes *turbulent*:

In turbulent flow, the air is disturbed and *drag* occurs; this slows the ball's flight. The effect becomes greater as the speed of the ball increases. It also depends on the size and mass of the ball. A large light ball slows down more than a small heavy one.

Investigation

A simple experiment will give an idea of this.

1   Take a selection of balls.
2   Find the mass and diameter of each; use the table on page 51 to help.
3   Throw each as far as you can. Use the same person, the same technique, and the same force for each ball.
4   Measure the length of each throw.
5   Don't forget your results table!

The surface of the ball does affect the amount of turbulence and drag. For example, the dimpled golf ball flies better than a smooth one.

Without air, in a vacuum, any ball would travel further. The graph shows the difference in range between cricket balls thrown in air and in a vacuum. Notice that the effect is greatest on the faster throws: the strong arm suffers more from air resistance than the weak arm.

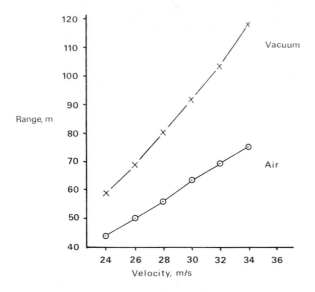

Except for colour, one snooker ball is very much like another: the same mass, the same diameter, the same surface texture. This is not true with balls used in other sports. As we shall see, the temperature of a squash ball, the shininess of a cricket ball, the spin of a tennis ball are all important variables. The critical features of a golf ball are its composition and its surface.

Traditional golf balls were made of an extremely long rubber thread, wound very tightly around a heavy core. The higher the compression, the greater the elasticity, the faster the ball flew.

The newer type of ball is solid, made of plastic. It compresses less on impact, so it travels even faster. The plastic dimpled cover is not needed now to hold the threat in place, but it is not there just to make it look nicer. The dimples increase the lift on the spinning ball, making it travel further.

The spin of a ball has an enormous effect on its flight. The spin produces extra lift by the *Magnus effect*. The pressure beneath the spinning ball is greater than the pressure above it, resulting in lift. There are some important factors which affect the amount of this spin-produced lift:

(a)   it is increased by a rough surface, hence the importance of dimples;
(b)   the amount of spin depends on the exact construction of the ball;
(c)   it alters the 'best' angle of projection from 45° to 20°.

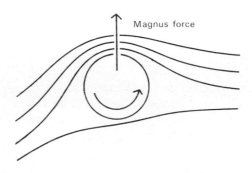

The relationship between angle of impact and the amount of spin-produced lift is interesting. A perfectly smooth ball projected at 45° with no spin at all would actually carry further than a 'normal' hit. The world's golf courses, however, are still waiting to see a golfer who can hit a perfect shot at 45° with a putter from a tee half a metre high!

Investigation

A simple experiment may give some idea of the effect of dimples, and compare different kinds of dimples. As measuring flow through the usual fluid, air, is difficult, we make use of a rather denser fluid – water, or, better still, oil.

1   Find a smooth (old, worn) golf ball, and one with good dimples. (A third one with hexagonal dimples will give an extra comparison.)
2   Fill a large measuring cylinder with liquid.
3   Hold one of the balls on the surface of the liquid.
4   Start a stop-clock as you release the ball.
5   Measure the time it takes to fall.
6   Repeat several times for each ball.

7 Tabulate your results, and work out the average rate for each ball.

8 Try spinning the ball to see whether this has any effect.

Is there any difference between the balls?

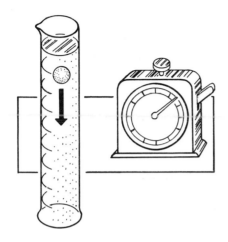

Speed

We have already seen that the speed of a golf ball depends on the force with which it is hit. This force depends largely on the speed at which the club is moving at the moment of impact.

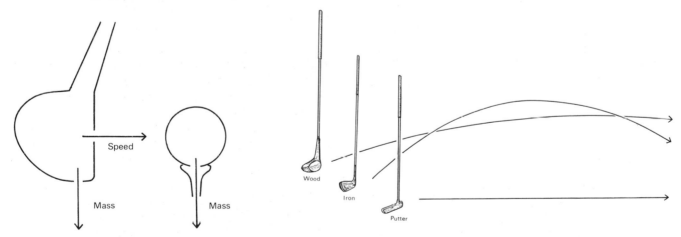

Wood

Iron

Putter

Speed

Mass

Mass

There is a direct relationship between the two speeds which we can calculate:

$$\frac{\text{speed of ball}}{\text{speed of club}} = \frac{(\text{mass of club} + \text{mass of ball})}{\text{mass of club} \times 1.7}$$

Try a regulation 46 g ball and a 200 g club.

This gives a result of 1.4: the ball will travel 1.4 times faster than did the club. You can vary the figures in the calculation to find out what would happen if you used a heavier (or lighter) club

and/or a heavier (or lighter) ball. But, for a normal club and a regulation ball, the ball will travel at 1.4 times the speed of the club. So a manufacturer claiming a 40% increase in speed off the tee would actually be saying nothing at all about his ball. The rules of golf set the maximum ball mass at 46 g. In the United States the ball must be at least 4.25 cm in diameter. In Britain the minimum is 4.1 cm.

The actual club used, of course, has much more effect than that of its mass on the speed of the ball. The drawing gives an idea of the range which can be expected from various clubs, and the sort of flight path.

The PROJECTILES computer program (page 108) will draw flight paths for different angles – but there is an extra factor: spin.

Angle	Spin, rev/s
20°	57
30°	83
40°	106

Spin

As the angle of the club face increases, there is an increase in the angle of take-off. This means less speed, but more spin. More spin, as we have seen, means more lift.

Spin also has an effect on the bounce of the ball when it finally completes its flight through the air. A golf ball normally has back spin. The more spin, the more sharply it bounces. With enough spin, it may even bounce back on itself. In other games, such as tennis, the ball may have forward spin as it bounces. The effects of spin on bounce are shown. The bounce of five balls landing at 30° is shown to depend on their spin.

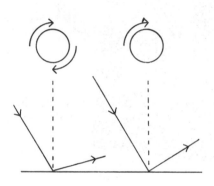

Much forward spin   Little forward spin

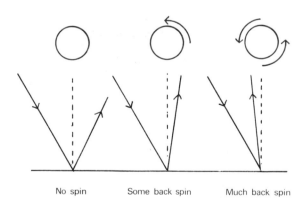

No spin   Some back spin   Much back spin

Forward spin = lower bounce
Back spin = higher bounce

Back spin

Top spin

Top spin

Top spin can be given to the ball by hitting it with the racket moving upwards across the ball. This spins the ball in such a way that the flight path dips. A much higher landing angle means that the ball *kicks* on bouncing, even though the spin makes the bounce angle slightly less than expected.

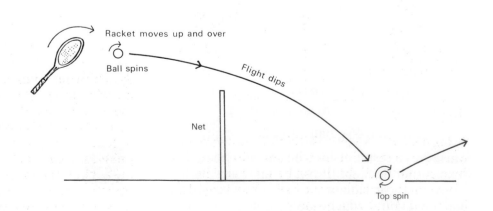

Racket moves up and over
Ball spins
Flight dips
Net
Top spin

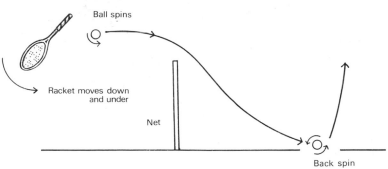

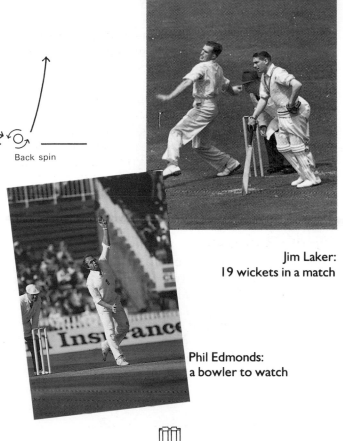

Jim Laker:
19 wickets in a match

Back spin

Back spin is produced by 'chopping' underneath the ball. The flight path is more looped, but the ball bounces higher because of the spin. It may even bounce back on itself. This is the drop-shot.

Spin and swing

These terms are often used in cricket. The swing produced by a fast bowler with the new ball is due to a balance between streamlined and turbulent flow. (See page 57 if you've forgotten these already!)

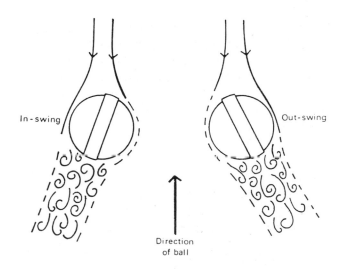

Phil Edmonds:
a bowler to watch

If the ball travels with the seam at an angle, the air is faced with a smooth (seamless) side and a roughened (seamed) side. Flow will be streamlined on the smooth side, turbulent on the seam side. It is the different types of flow which make the ball swing in the air.

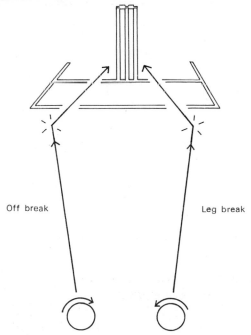

Swing can only occur if the flight is fast enough, and if the seam points in the same direction throughout the flight. It can be increased by roughening one side of the ball. (You should be able to work out which side.)

Spin bowling remains an art even when the science is understood. The spinning ball skids when it meets the pitch; the amount of sideways skid depends on the amount of spin, and on the length of time for which the skidding lasts. After the skid phase, the ball rolls in a straight line. The softer the wicket, the longer the contact, and the more skidding. Hence cricketing talk such as a 'sticky' wicket being a 'real turner'.

Spin, swerve and stun

The game of snooker takes its name, not from the potting of balls, but from the situation in which the path of the cue ball is blocked by another ball. An experienced player is able to swerve the cue ball in a curved path, so as to miss the obstacle.

The theory is similar to that of spin bowling: spin the cue ball so that it skids sideways, before rolling straight on.

Less skilful players make use of the cushion in such a situation. Here, two scientific principles are important. The importance of cueing at the right height (about 3.5 cm to avoid skidding) has already been discussed. The law of reflection we tend to take rather for granted. Like light on a mirror, a ball will bounce off the cushion at the same angle as it arrived.

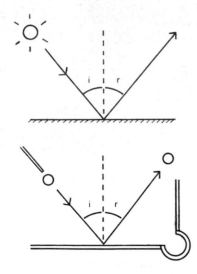

Angle of incidence (i) = Angle of reflection (r)

The most impressive part of professional snooker is not the potting of the balls, but the way in which the cue ball is directed ready for the next shot. To do this, players make use of *top*, *bottom* and *side* spins.

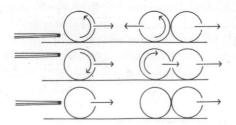

A cue ball struck low down will gain bottom spin. On hitting another ball it will roll back towards the cue. A ball being struck above the 70% height will gain top spin. It will move forward faster after impact as this spin is turned into rolling. A *stunned* ball hit dead centre will skid without rolling. It will stop 'dead' on impact, staying where it it. (This technique is also familiar to the shove ha'penny player!)

The cue ball may also be given 'side' – that is, side spin. This means that it is hit away from the vertical centre. After impact it will alter its direction of travel.

Temperature

A squash ball is rather different to those met so far. Most important is its change of elasticity with temperature. As it warms up it becomes more and more elastic; its 'bounciness' increases. It bounces faster and further. This is why squash players need to 'warm up' the ball, as well as themselves. The graph shows the amount of variation.

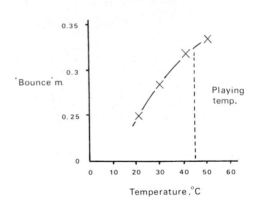

The oval ball

Most of the ideas discussed in these chapters can be applied to any kind of ball. The rugby ball (or the American football) is, however, rather different. The ovoid shape means that its flight path is more complex. There are, though, a few simple investigations and explanations which are worth looking at.

The most important changes in rugby in recent years have been:

(a)   styles of goal-kicking;
(b)   spin passes and throws;
(c)   torpedo (*screw*) kicks.

Investigation

An apparently simple study of goal-kicking styles is full of difficulties. Unless we can build a goal-kicking machine, there are bound to be differences between kicks, even with the same players.

1 Select a suitable point on the pitch, e.g. exact centre, on the 22 m line.
2 Take 10 kicks at goal, using the same style each time. Record the number of successes.
3 Repeat for other styles.
4 Repeat all the styles from different places. (Do each 10 times again!)

Does any style seem more efficient and accurate? Why have so many kickers adopted the 'round the corner' style? Are different techniques better for long kicks? Does the wind affect different styles in different ways? These are the kind of questions which the sport scientist can investigate, and try to explain.

At least with spin effects there's a definite answer: streamlining. The torpedo pass, throw-in and kick all try to do the same thing. They try to make sure that the ball travels *point-first*, giving the minimum of air resistance. This reduces the drag, and gives greater distance for the same impact force.

Problem page

■ Design and make a machine to hit any ball with a *standard* force.

Use your machine to investigate the effect of changing mass, size, surface etc.

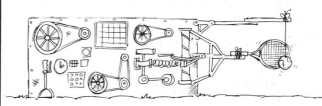

■ Investigate the contact time and impact force for both *correct* and *incorrect* combinations of balls and 'hitters'.

Use your findings to devise novel games, e.g. baseball bat/rugby ball.

7

How the body reacts

Reflex save earns replay

NERVOUS SEMI-FINAL

Adrenaline flows, then champagne

Many of our ideas about how the body reacts during sport comes from statements like these. We read them in newspapers, hear them from commentators. Many of them are misleading; some are completely wrong. In this chapter, and in the next, we will look at what scientists call *physiology* – how the body works.

Senses

We often speak of the 'five senses'.

Really, there are six:

Of these, taste and smell are not of much use to the sportsman. Next come hearing and touch (including temperature and pain), with the most important being sight (vision) and 'muscle sense'. Let's start with this last one, as it is the least familiar.

Stretch receptors

Inside muscles (and joints and tendons) are small sense organs called *proprioceptors*, or stretch receptors. These measure the stretch of muscles and tendons, the angles and pressures of joints. This is the basis of the system which keeps the body upright, and keeps a check on movements.

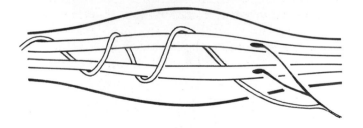

The more a proprioceptor is stretched – by whatever force – the more the muscle contracts. This contraction, which maintains body posture, is called muscle *tone*.

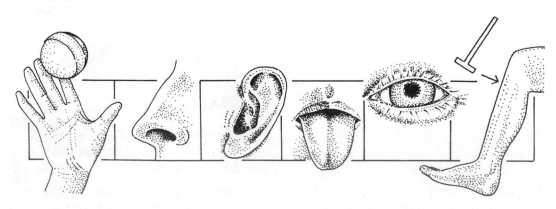

Little stretch
Little muscle tone

Muscles stretched
Tone maintains posture

Muscles very stretched
More tone needed

Knee-jerk reflex

Much body movement is controlled by reflexes. We are not conscious of everything our senses receive from outside (or inside). Reflexes mean that we can avoid danger (blinking, dropping hot objects) or adjust the body (digest food, cough, balance, change pupil size) without thinking. One of the best known of these is the knee-jerk reflex. If you hit the tendon, the leg kicks. Follow the route which the nerve impulses (signals) take:

2 Cross one leg over the other, heel against stool.
3 Tap just below the knee. This will start the timer.
4 As the leg kicks, the timer will stop.
5 Take several measurements of reflex time, and find the average.

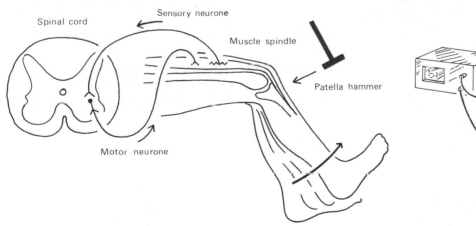

Spinal cord
Sensory neurone
Muscle spindle
Patella hammer
Motor neurone

Investigation

You can try this for yourself. It's quite easy to use this to measure the speed of body reflexes.

1 Connect 'hammer' (soft!), knee, heel and stool to a timer; wrap aluminium foil around them to make good electrical contact.

Reflexes

When a commentator talks of a goalkeeper making a *reflex* save, is he using the word correctly? A true reflex is:

(a) unconscious – no thought is needed,
(b) repeatable – the same response every time,
(c) universal – everyone reacts in the same way.

6   Record the time.
7   Reset timer, switch 1 and switch 2 (in that order).
8   Take several measurements, and work out the mean reaction time.

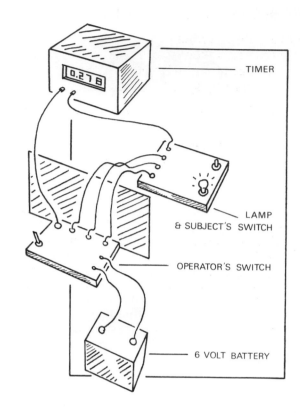

Most people's reaction to a ball speeding at their head is to get out of the way. Only a sportsman is likely to try to catch it – or to deliberately head it! It is often said, therefore, that a goalkeeper's action may be a *conditioned* reflex. The classic example is of Pavlov's dogs which became conditioned to produce saliva on hearing a bell, rather than on smelling food. Now do you understand the drawing?

Others argue that sportsmen's responses have to be learned and practised.

Reaction time

True reflexes are the quickest way of turning a stimulus, such as a bright light, into a response – narrowing the pupils. They are not, however, what we are usually concerned with in sport.

The time which is important is the reaction time. This is the time between stimulus and response in a conscious action such as hitting a ball or jumping a hurdle. It is quite easy to measure using the equipment shown.

1   Connect the timer and switches.
2   Make sure the timer starts when switch 1 is on, and stops when switch 2 is pressed.
3   Set up the system so that the subject can't see switch 1 or the operator.
4   The operator starts the timer and switches on the light, by means of switch 1.
5   The subject presses switch 2 as soon as he sees the light. This stops the timer.

Results tend to follow the sort of pattern shown in the graph: some improvement at first, but a definite limit. (It will of course make a difference where the subject rests his hand.)

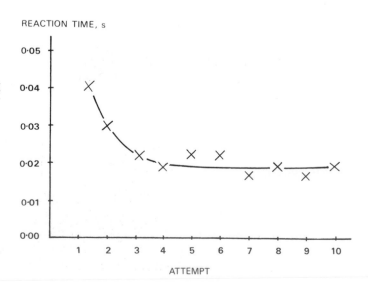

Simple method to measure reaction time

How far can a metre rule fall before you catch it?

Two factors decide: the force of gravity, accelerating it downwards, and your reaction time.

The simple formula is: $s = ut + \frac{1}{2}at^2$

where s displacement
    t time taken
    a acceleration (gravity, 9.81 m s^{-2})
    u starting speed (0 in this case)

Here are (a) a table with enough figures for a graph;
    (b) a graph;
    (c) a computer program.

(a)

Time, s	0	0.05	0.10	0.15	0.20
Displacement, m	0	0.01	0.05	0.11	0.20
Time, s	0.25	0.30	0.35	0.40	0.45
Displacement, m	0.31	0.44	0.60	0.78	0.99

(b)

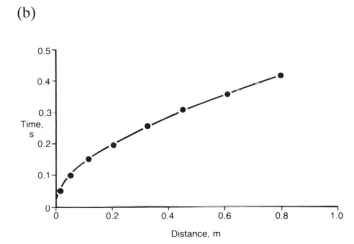

Time, s (vertical axis) — Distance, m (horizontal axis)

(c) Appendix A   see page 108.

The false start

Reaction times have interesting effects on races such as 100 m.

A good start

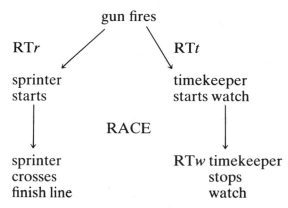

gun fires

RTr RTt

sprinter starts   timekeeper starts watch

RACE

sprinter crosses finish line   RTw timekeeper stops watch

If RTr = RTt = RTw, then timing is accurate. But what if they are different?

A false start

sprinter starts

RTs

starter reacts: false start

But what if the starter fires the gun before he can react?

It is quite easy to make a 'false start detector'.

If the runner leaves before the switch is closed, the clock will not start.

But there is a fault with this system. No athlete can react in less than, say, 0.1 s. But a false start will not be detected if the circuit is broken at any time – even 0.001 s – after the clock starts.

Answer: more complex electrical circuitry – or use a computer. . . .

(See Appendix A, page 108, for a suitable Logo program using a simple interface.)

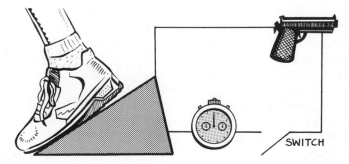

SWITCH

Vision

Ask a sportsperson which sense is the most important, and most will say sight or vision. It is certainly the one which is the most well developed.

How do we see at all?
How do we see in stereo (depth)?
How do we see movement?
How do we see colour?

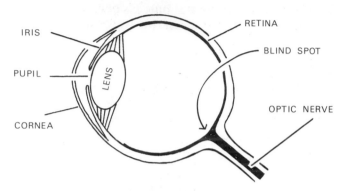

Our eyes have a complicated structure, but what they do is really quite simple. Light is bent by cornea and lens as it passes through the pupil; it is then focused on the retina, where cells send impulses (messages) to the brain, where we 'see' the light.

The lens and cornea are both convex or *converging*. The image on the retina is actually *inverted* (upside down), but the brain turns it the *right way up*.

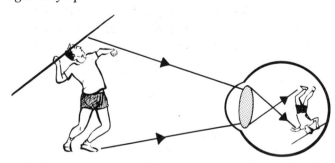

Seeing in stereo

Seeing in stereo is very important in sport. Without binocular (two-eyes) vision we could not judge distance. England cricketer Colin Milburn and goalkeeper Gordon Banks both retired after losing the sight of one eye. You can get an idea of how important it is to have two eyes with this simple experiment.

1 Hold the book flat, just below eye level.
2 Close one eye.
3 Look along the dotted line on the edge of the paper.
4 Try to touch the ball.
5 Move the book to see how close you were.
6 Now try again, with both eyes open.
   If you can't do it now, see an optician!

It's more difficult to judge distance with one eye because the brain works out distances by comparing angles. It measures the angle of the light entering each eye. It's a similar method to finding your position with a map and compass: you need two compass bearings. One compass reading, like one eye, may give a fair idea, but it is never accurate.

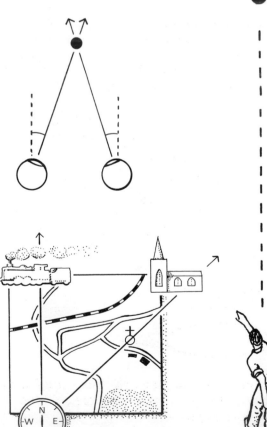

Some sports make more demands than others on good vision, especially judging distance. Imagine a game of bowls between Sir Francis Drake and Lord Nelson. Nelson's one arm would have been only a small disadvantage (balance?) compared with his one eye.

Seeing movement

Being able to see movement clearly is another useful ability for a sportsperson. We often speak of players 'having a good eye', and we use phrases like 'keep your eye on the ball'. These remind us that we are able to change the angle and focus of the eyes.

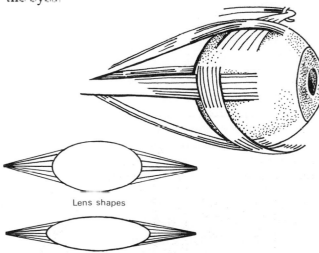

Lens shapes

This is done by various muscles. Some are fixed to the lens and change its shape. Others hold the whole eyeball in position. These are able to move the eye in almost any direction.

Our eyes are best at seeing objects straight ahead. This is because there are more cells in the central part of the retina. When we see something 'out of the corner of the eye', we may only just be aware of it. Yet this ability is vital in sport, as it gives a chance to turn the eyes or the head for a clearer view. Scientists call this *peripheral vision*.

Try this experiment on peripheral vision.

1. Get someone to look straight ahead.
2. Hold a coloured object behind him.
3. Move it slowly round, past his ear.
4. Record the positions of the object when he can.
   (a) see it,
   (b) be sure what it is,
   (c) be certain of its colour.

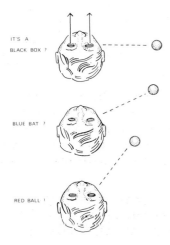

IT'S A BLACK BOX ?

BLUE BAT ?

RED BALL !

You may know that each eye has a 'blind spot'. This is the point at which the optic nerve leaves the eye, to carry impulses to the brain. At this point, there are no light sensitive cells, so any light landing here is not 'seen'. Use the cricketers below to discover your blind spot:

1. Close your right eye.
2. Hold the book at arm's length.
3. Look at the bowler, with your left eye.
4. You will be aware of the batsman, but do not look directly at him.
5. Slowly bring the book nearer.
6. The batsman will 'disappear' when his image falls on the blind spot of the left eye.
7. Keep bringing the book nearer.
8. The batsman will reappear.
   You may be able to 'lose' the ball!
9. Try with the left eye shut to make the bowler vanish.

Pupils

The eyes' pupils are not actual structures. They are just *holes* in the coloured iris. Each pupil is surrounded by two sets of muscles. One set makes it larger, so more light gets in. The other set makes it smaller, so that less light enters the eye. This change is reflex, depending on the level of light. You can show this quite easily.

1 Notice the size of the pupils in 'normal' light.
2 Shine a bright light onto the eye.
  Notice what happens to the pupils.
3 Make the room dim by drawing blinds or switching off lights.
  Notice what happens to the pupils now.

In very bright light we tend to squint. This gives extra protection to the eyes until the pupils and retina have altered. Cricketers are always advised not to go in to bat straight from a dark pavilion.

Colour vision

Colour vision is important in only a few sports. Look again at the list on page 25. Which of these would colour-blindness make difficult? Why?

We see colour in a way similar to that in which a colour TV makes its colour. A colour TV has three tubes: red, green and blue. The retina of the eye has three kinds of cells for colour vision: red cones, green cones and blue cones. The fourth kind of cell – rods – work only in dim light, and in *monochrome* (black and white).

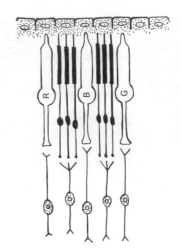

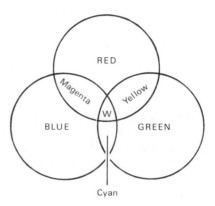

'For those of you watching in black and white, the yellow ball is directly behind the pink.' *TV Snooker Commentator*

Floodlights

To most people, sport is an opposite to work. It provides relaxation, a chance to concentrate on something other than life's problems. Much sport therefore takes place on outside working hours. For outdoor sports in winter this means that some kind of artificial lighting is necessary.

There are three scientific questions to answer:

(i)   How bright is the lighting?
(ii) How much energy is required?
(iii) How will the lighting affect players' vision?

One problem with lighting is the *inverse square law*. This means that doubling the distance from a light gives only one quarter of the brightness. For example:

Distance, m	1	2	3	4	5	6	10	12
Brightness, lumens	144	36	16	9	5.76	4	1.44	1

Terrible pitch but terrific floodlights!

shades of grey only.) The table shows the effects of coloured lighting. Try it for yourself.

	Coloured light					
Actual colour	**Red**	**Green**	**Blue**	**Yellow**	**Cyan**	**Magenta**
Red	red	black	black	red	black	red
Green	black	green	black	green	green	black
Blue	black	black	blue	black	blue	blue
Yellow	red	green	black	yellow	green	red
Cyan	black	green	blue	green	cyan	blue
Magenta	red	black	blue	red	blue	magenta

Colours of objects under different lighting

For a minimum-size soccer pitch, four sets of floodlights have to each illuminate 1250 m². To prevent dazzle, damage and disturbance, the lights must be fairly high above the pitch. The inverse sqaure law means that a large brightness is needed, consuming a lot of power. A professional ground may have to comply with special regulations, such as those of UEFA. Southampton FC have ninety-six mercury halide lamps giving a total of over 150 kW.

Players' vision will be affected as the ability to see detail is dependent on light intensity. Colour vision, too, is affected by both strength and colour of lighting. (In dim light, vision is restricted to

Soccer – the traditional 'working man's sport' in Britain – has been played under floodlights since 1878, although the first floodlit Football League match was not played until 1956, at Fratton Park, Portsmouth. Other sports followed, the most recent being cricket. The breakaway World Series Cricket introduced floodlit cricket to Australia. Restricted length evening matches became popular, and soon reached the 'official' game. Innovations such as a white ball, coloured pads and black sight-screens were found to improve visibility for the players.

Hearing

It is difficult to assess the importance of hearing in sport. In team games, talking (and shouting!) are often valuable. For individual events, however, any sound may be disturbing. There is a balance between information and noise; like a badly-tuned radio, it may be important or distracting. (Engineers talk about the *signal to noise ratio*.)

Try to think of some sounds which are (a) helpful, (b) distracting, or (c) have no effect.

As with vision, we hear in stereo; the brain compares the volume in each ear to work out the direction of sound. The ear itself, like the eye, is a complicated structure which does an apparently simple job. Sound waves vibrate the ear-drum; the ear-bones (*ossicles*) then amplify these vibrations and pass them on to fluid in the cochlea; receptor cells produce nerve impulses which the brain 'hears' as sound.

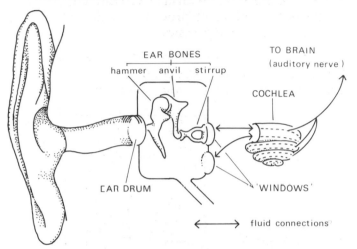

Human ear bones form a very efficient amplifier. The pressure at the stirrup is 22 times that at the hammer.

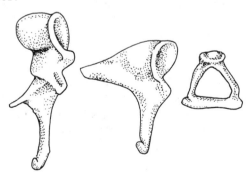

Because of the vast range of hearing of both volume (loudness) and frequency (pitch), logarithmic scales are often used: see page 22. The decibel (dB) is an example of this. A rise of 10 dB (=1 Bel) means 10 times as loud! The minimum most people can hear is 0 dB – not 0 sound, but $1 \times 10^{-12}/W\,m^{-2}$. The maximum is about 120 dB (=1 W/m²), a million million times louder – above this level permanent ear damage can occur.

Audible frequencies range from 20 Hz (Hertz = cycles per second) to about 20 kHz – rather less in males and as we get older. The human voice can produce sounds between 80 Hz and 1 kHz.

To be heard above the noise of a crowd, or other background noise, an important sport sound must be either:
(a)   a higher frequency, e.g. a referee's whistle, or
(b)   a greater volume, e.g. a starting pistol.

These are both illustrated in the graphs below.

Referee's whistle

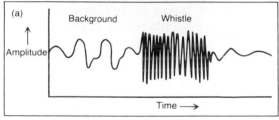

Starting gun

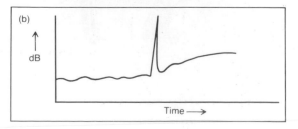

8

Body in action

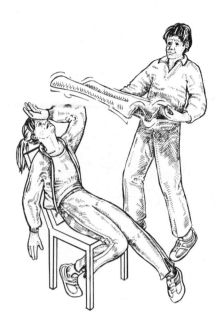

Effects of exercise

While you do any activities – or any sport – you will notice several changes in your body:

- heart beats stronger and faster
- breathing quickens and deepens
- body temperature increases
- sweating
- aching muscles

All these *physiological* changes have a cause and a purpose. In this chapter we will look at some of them in more detail.

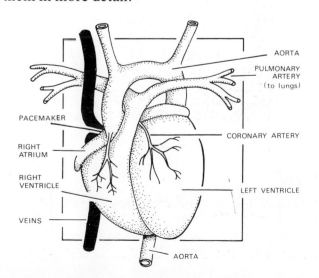

Heart beat

This starts in the pacemaker, but is controlled by nerves and hormones. During exercise, it is mainly *adrenaline* which produces changes in heart beat and blood pressure.

Find your pulse, on the thumb side of the wrist. Press with two fingers, and count the number of beats in a minute. This is your pulse rate.

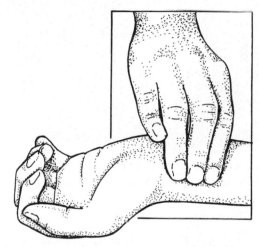

ECG

ECG (electrocardiograph) is an examination of the electrical activity in the heart. Sports clinics, doctors and a number of schools have the equipment to record and display an ECG.

A single heart-beat shown on an ECG trace

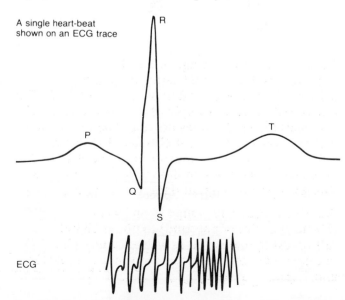

ECG

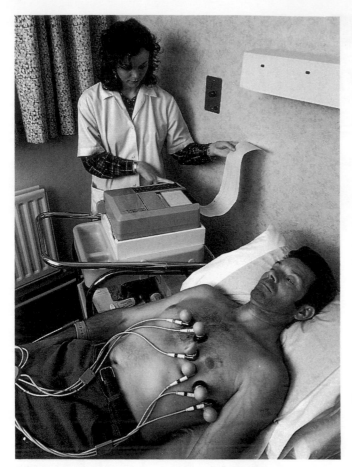

ECG being taken

Note: these times are for a resting heart:
75 beats/min = 0.8 s/beat $(75 \times 0.8 = 60)$

At 180 beats/min, the total
cycle is only 0.33 s/beat $(180 \times 0.33 = 60)$

Most of this change is produced by reducing the
rest phase (diastole) to less than 0.1 s.

Blood circulation

On each circuit, blood passes twice through the
heart. Once – the right side – on its way to the
lungs to collect oxygen. Then again – the left side
– en route to the rest of the body to deliver the
oxygen to muscles and other tissues.

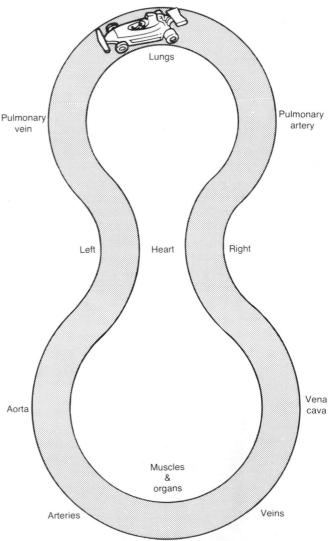

Heart muscle

Heart muscle is a special kind of muscle – cardiac
– which contracts repeatedly without tiring: 70
beats per minute is nearly 37 million beats per
year!

Compare it with the other types of muscle on page
76.

The heart is really two pairs of pumps, working in
parallel. Each heart beat is made up of three
phases:

Phase	What happens	time, s	ECG code
atrial systole	atria contract	0.1	P
ventricular systole	ventricles contract	0.3	QRS
diastole	relaxation	0.4	T

Arteries

Arteries are very muscular. They help the blood
on its way by squeezing. One of the effects of
exercise is to increase the size and strength of the
main artery, the aorta.

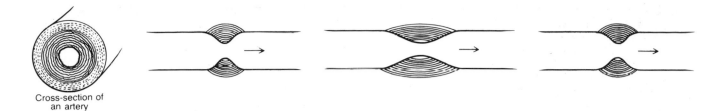

Cross-section of
an artery

Capillaries

Capillaries are extremely narrow (the size of a single blood cell) and very thin (only one cell thick). This means that blood flows very slowly and that oxygen can diffuse into the surrounding cells. Muscle capillaries can enlarge by a factor of 5 during strenuous exercise. Because blood flow depends on (diameter)^4 this means an increase in flow of $5^4 = 625$ times!

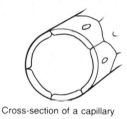

Cross-section of a capillary

Veins

Veins have thinner walls than arteries and less muscle. The pressure is very low and blood flow is helped by the contractions of nearby muscles. Valves prevent back flow.

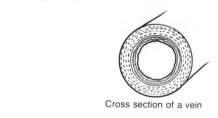

Cross section of a vein

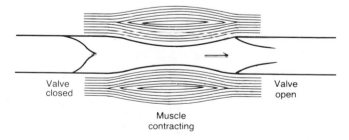

Valve closed   Valve open

Muscle contracting

Blood pressure

Blood pressure is often said to be '120 over 80'. This means a systolic pressure of 120 mm mercury and a diastolic pressure of 80 mm mercury. These are 'average' rather than 'normal' values, and only apply to the main arteries. The pressure changes throughout the system, as the graph shows:

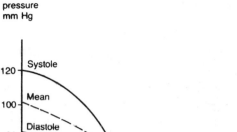

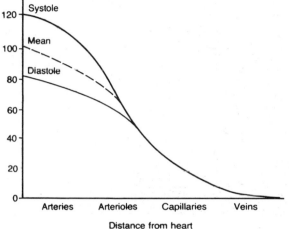

Blood flow

Blood flow depends, among other things, on pressure and vessel diameter. At rest, the amount of blood flowing to the various organs is as shown.

Organ	Blood flow, litres/min
bone	0.25
brain	0.7
bronchi	0.1
heart	0.2
kidneys	1.1
liver	1.35
muscles	0.75
skin	0.3
thyroid gland	0.05
others	0.2
TOTAL	**5.0**

The diagram shows what happens during exercise to the relative flow through some of the organs.

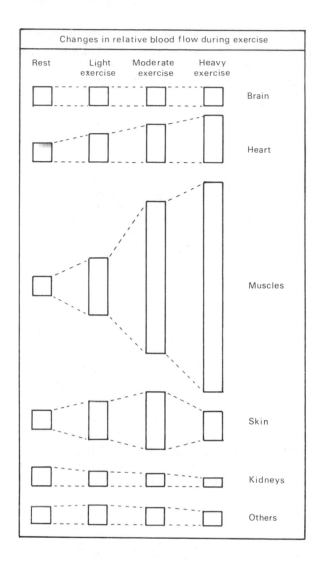

dependent on the number of red blood cells, as it is the red *haemoglobin* which carries the oxygen. It is particularly important at high altitudes, as was shown by the 1968 Olympic Games in Mexico City.

A runner from high altitude

Blood

Blood itself is about 55% liquid plasma (various substances dissolved in water) and 45% cells (red, white and platelets). Females have a slightly smaller blood volume and a lower number of red blood cells:

	Female	Male
Blood volume, ml/kg	65	75
Red cells, ml	4 800 000	5 400 000

The main functions of blood are:

transport of oxygen
waste materials
food
hormones

regulation of pH (acidity)
temperature

Perhaps the most important function for sports activity is oxygen transport. This is very

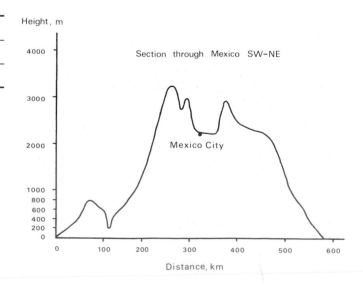

Only those athletes who had spent long periods living at high altitudes were able to compete at near normal standard. Living in such conditions leads to an increase in the numbers of oxygen-carrying red blood cells, and hence more efficient oxygen transport. It was no coincidence that all the distance races were won by native altitude dwellers (e.g. Ethiopians) or by athletes who had spent long training periods at altitude. Other athletes suffered from the same sort of altitude sickness common to mountaineers.

A controversial method of increasing oxygen capacity of the blood is blood 'doping' or 'dumping'. The procedure would be to take some blood from the athlete (like a blood donor) and store it. He or she would replace it naturally in a few weeks. Just before an important race this blood could be given back to the athlete – a transfusion. The body would then have more blood to carry more oxygen.

Muscles

Muscles need energy. This energy comes from food, mainly converted to glucose (sugar) for use. To work most efficiently, muscles also need plenty of oxygen. Both glucose and oxygen are brought in the blood; wastes such as carbon dioxide are also carried away in the blood. This process of getting energy is called *respiration*.

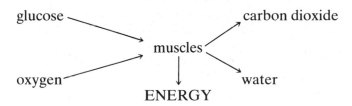

When muscles do extra work, more glucose and oxygen are needed. More blood must flow to the muscles. The heart beats faster, the blood vessels narrow to raise the pressure. More blood is sent to the muscles rather than other organs. We have seen what happens to the blood flow as exercise becomes more strenuous.

Finally, however, it becomes impossible to get enough oxygen to the muscles. They have then to use a different method of getting energy. Glucose is still used, but now the waste product is lactic acid.

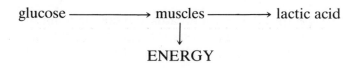

Lactic acid is poisonous. After a while, there is enough of it to make the muscle ache. Eventually, it causes cramp, and the muscle will no longer contract. The athlete is forced to rest while the blood brings fresh supplies of oxygen.

Production of energy with oxygen is called *aerobic* respiration; production of energy without oxygen is called *anaerobic* respiration.

Race	% anaerobic respiration
100 m	100–95
200 m	95
400 m	83
800 m	66
1 500 m	50
5 000 m	20
10 000 m	10
marathon	2

A sprinter can run 100 m without using much oxygen. During the 10 s or so of the race he respires anaerobically, and so builds up an *oxygen debt*. The high level of lactic acid means that extra oxygen is needed after the race, as the debt is paid back. In longer races, the amount of anaerobic respiration is reduced so that large amounts of lactic acid do not build up. There is therefore a smaller oxygen debt.

Suffering from cramp

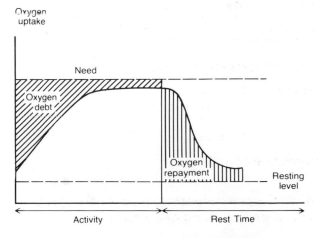

Like most debts, there is 'interest' to pay. The oxygen needed to dispose of the lactic acid is more than would have been used in aerobic respiration.

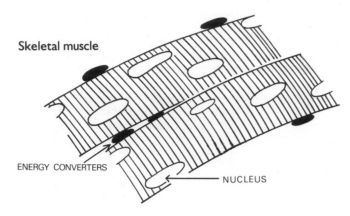

Skeletal muscle

ENERGY CONVERTERS

NUCLEUS

Skeletal muscle

This type of muscle contains large numbers of energy converters – *mitochondria* – in which the release of energy from food takes place. We know now that there are two types of this muscle: *fast twitch* and *slow twitch*. The table shows the main differences.

Fast twitch	Slow twitch
white	red
power	endurance
anaerobic	aerobic
extensors	flexors

The distribution of fast and slow fibres has been studied in runners. Some results are shown.

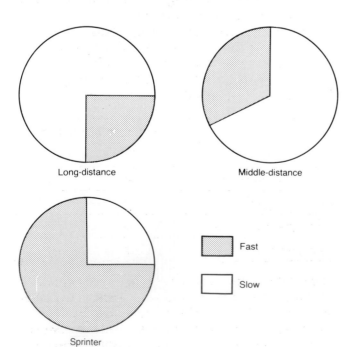

Long-distance

Middle-distance

Fast

Slow

Sprinter

Breathing

Breathing is also greatly affected by exercise. However fast the heart beats, the blood can't carry enough oxygen if it isn't getting into the lungs. Two investigations will help measure the efficiency of your lungs.

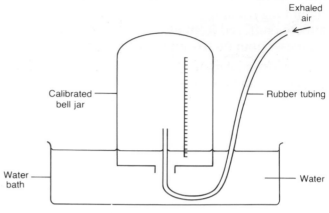

Exhaled air

Calibrated bell jar

Rubber tubing

Water bath

Water

Investigation A

1 Set up the apparatus shown above.
2 Breathe normally, blowing one of the breaths through the tubing.
3 Measure your *tidal volume*.
4 Fill the jar again with water.
5 Take deep breaths, then blow out as much as you can through the tubing.
6 Measure your *vital capacity*.

Volume

Total lung capacity

Tidal volume

Vital capacity

Residual volume

Count the number of breaths you take in a minute – in and out counts as one. This is your breathing rate. You may find it better to get someone else to

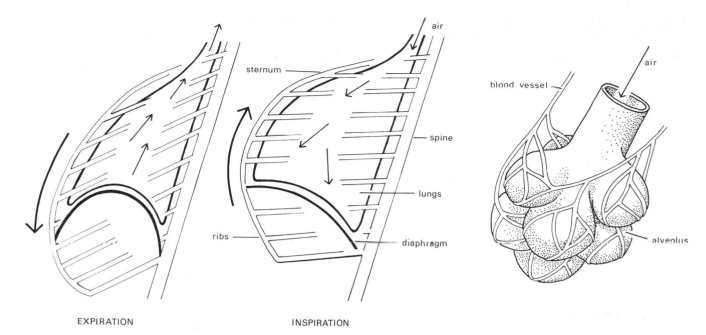

EXPIRATION   INSPIRATION

count, as people often breathe differently when they are aware of it.

For breathing in (*inspiration*) two sets of muscles are at work. The diaphragm is pulled down. The ribs are pulled upwards and outwards. This makes the chest expand, so lung pressure falls. Air is forced in from outside.

Two other sets of antagonistic muscles contract for breathing out (*expiration*). The diaphragm is pulled up and the ribs down and in. A smaller chest cavity means greater pressure, so air is forced out.

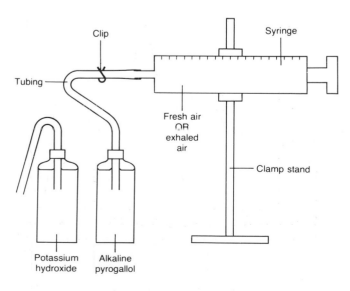

Investigation B

As well as how much air you can get into your lungs, the efficiency of breathing depends on how much oxygen you can remove from this air. The second investigation gives some idea of this.

1. Set up the apparatus shown below left. To measure oxygen, use alkaline pyrogallol. To measure carbon dioxide use potassium hydroxide solution. **CARE: both liquids are corrosive**
2. Fill the syringe with fresh air.
3. Fit the syringe in position, and open the clip connecting the alkaline pyrogallol.
4. Read the volume (originally 100 cm³) now that some gas has been absorbed.
5. Repeat the procedure, using potassium hydroxide instead of the alkaline pyrogallol.
6. Repeat the investigation, using air which has been breathed out (exhaled or expired).
7. Compare your results with those in the table:

	Fresh air	Exhaled air
original volume, cm³	100	100
after CO_2 removal, cm³	100	96
volume CO_2, cm³	0	4
after oxygen removal, cm³	80	84
volume oxygen, cm³	20	16

The most important structures in oxygen uptake are the *alveoli*. These are tiny air-sacs, at the ends of the tubes (*bronchioles*) in the lungs. Each alveolus is surrounded by capillary blood vessels; oxygen crosses into the blood, carbon dioxide out.

Body temperature

It's obvious that we produce heat whenever we do any sort of physical activity. What is less obvious is what happens to the body temperature at this time. Does it go up? Stay the same? Or does all that sweating make it actually go down? (See page 93).

To try to answer that question we first need to know what the body's temperature is at rest, under 'normal' conditions. To measure it, we use a special clinical thermometer.

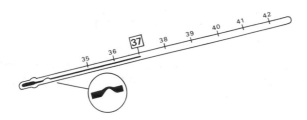

This is kept under the tongue for a minute, then taken out and the temperature read. The kink in the mercury thread means that the thermometer reads the same after it has been taken out of the mouth. (What would happen with an ordinary thermometer?)

37° C is often said to be 'normal' body temperature. What does this mean? Is it really normal?

No. It's the mean (or average) temperature. Yours may be as much as a degree more or less and still be normal – normal, that is, for you. Each person has his or her own normal temperature: the population has an average. It will be useful to record your own body temperature. You can compare it with the mean, and see what happens to it during activity.

Sweating

Not all the energy produced in respiration is turned into muscle action. Some is turned into heat. The body can tolerate a small rise in temperature but, after a while, sweating begins. Sweat pours from the pores in the skin. Once on the surface, it evaporates. To evaporate, energy is needed; this energy comes from the heat of the body. As heat is lost, so the body temperature falls.

For every 1 g of water evaporated, 2260 joules of energy are needed. This latent heat loss cools the body. The loss in sweat of water and salt, however, does cause problems.

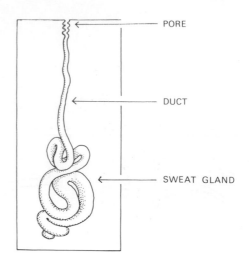

Under normal conditions, our water content is controlled:

water IN   =   water OUT
food + drink   urine + sweat

The diagram below shows how the body controls salt and water balance by means of hormones. This is a good example (simplified!) of self-regulation.

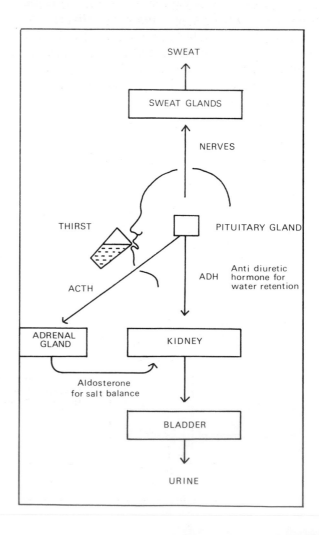

In hot conditions, we sweat more and produce less urine. However, unlike panting dogs, we lose salt as well as body heat and water when we sweat. (You can show this by simply tasting your own sweat, or by evaporating some on a microscope slide. or by mixing some with silver nitrate solution.) This salt has to be replaced so that the body fluids stay the same. Otherwise, cramp may result, or even actual collapse. Drinking pure water is all right in small amounts, but large quantities should be slightly salted.

water + salt	→	normal
no water	→	fainting, collapse
no salt	→	cramp, collapse

The watering stations in between the feeding points in the marathon may cool the athletes, but they may not be enough to maintain normal body function. Marathon runners reach towards the limits of human performance.

Hormones: chemical 'messengers'

Many of the body's activities go on for a long time. Nerves are not suited for the control of all of these. Instead, many reactions are controlled by chemical messengers – hormones.

The hormone most concerned with physical activity is *adrenaline*. Adrenaline is very similar to a substance produced by certain nerves. It has several very important effects:

- raises blood pressure
- increases heart rate
- makes more glucose available
- enlarges passages in lungs

Because of its production under stress, adrenaline is sometimes known as the hormone for 'flight, fight or fright'.

One of the actions of adrenaline is to encourage the production of glucose. Liver and muscle cells store glucose as the starch-like *glycogen*. Adrenaline speeds up the conversion of glycogen to glucose which then passes into the blood. With the increases in blood pressure and heart beat, both food and oxygen can reach the muscles more quickly.

Another hormone – *insulin* – pushes glucose into muscle cells. There it can be used to produce energy, or converted into glycogen for future use.

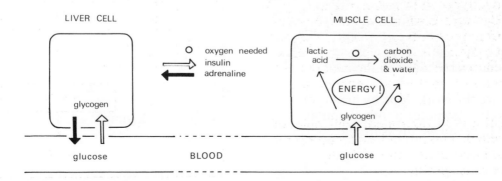

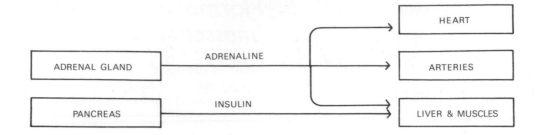

Its effect is to reduce the level of glucose in the blood. Diabetics have too little insulin, and cannot get enough glucose into the muscles. Activity for them may mean a dangerously high level of glucose in the blood. They can take part in sport, but need to carefully control their diet and/or inject insulin regularly.

Efficiency

Most machines are not very efficient. As much as 80 per cent of the chemical energy in the fuel ends up as heat, only 20 per cent as useful kinetic energy. Human machines (muscles) are better than most mechanical devices, but they still convert less than half the energy of food into useful work. And, of course, some of this kinetic energy may be wasted by poor technique. Useful work is, however, more difficult to measure than total physical work.

Efficiency can be defined as

$$\text{efficiency} = \frac{\text{useful work done} \times 100}{\text{energy used}}\%$$

We can measure the work done by means of step-ups, bicycle ergometer or other similar methods. But how can we measure the energy used up?

The rate at which the body uses energy is called the *metabolic rate*. Even at rest this varies from person to person. Endomorphs tend to have low resting metabolic rates; ectomorphs high rates. We can get an idea of the metabolic rate by measuring the amount of oxygen used up. Earlier in the chapter we collected enough data to do this:

volume of air per breath (litres)
×
per cent oxygen removed
×
number of breaths per minute
÷
100

This will give the volume of oxygen used per minute. The amount of energy this produces depends exactly on the 'fuel' being used: glucose gives more energy per litre of oxygen than fat. The table shows how this varies:

Food	Energy, kJ/litre oxygen
glucose	21.1
mixed	20.1
fat	19.6

If we now multiply the amount of oxygen used per minute by this factor (19.6, 20.1 or 21.1), we will get a value for the energy used in a minute. For a mixed diet,

energy used = oxygen uptake × 20.1
  kJ/min   litres/min

Efficiency is then given by

work done (kJ)
÷
length of activity (mins)
×
100
÷
energy used (kJ/min)

9

What is fitness?

In general use, 'fitness' means being in good athletic condition, active and healthy. In sport science we need to be able to measure degrees of fitness, so we have to use a more precise definition.

There are really two different aspects of fitness. One is the ability to perform athletic tasks, to do physical work. We would not describe as fit someone who was unable to run upstairs. The second is the speed and ease of recovery from an activity. If, after running a short distance, we take ten minutes to catch our breath and for our heart to slow down, we can hardly be fit.

Work, energy and power

Scientists define work in terms of force applied, and the distance the force moves:

WORK　　=　FORCE　×　DISTANCE
joules　　　　newtons　　　metres

So, if your 500 N* body jumps a height of 1 m, you have done $500 \times 1 = 500$ J of work.

* You may recall from Chapter 2 that there is often confusion over 'mass' and 'weight'. For work on fitness we need to use weight, in newtons. If you have

platform scales which measure in newtons (N), use these to find you body weight. If not, you can get a rough value by multiplying your body mass (in kg) by 10: body weight (N) = body mass (kg) $\times$ 10.

Energy is a different way of looking at work: to do 500 J of work needs 500 J of energy.

Power is the rate of doing work. To do 100 J of work in 1 s takes much more power than doing it in 10 s or 1 minute.

POWER　　=　WORK　÷　TIME
watts　　　　joules　　　seconds

The table gives a few examples.

force, N	distance, m	work, J	time, s	power, W
500	2	1000	10	100
10	100	1000	50	20
100	6	600	60	
500	100		10	

Step-ups, pull-ups, press-ups

Step-ups

Step-ups are one of the simplest, and most useful, exercises in sport science.

1　Find a bench, box or similar about 0.5 m high.
2　Measure its exact height, in metres.
3　Step up onto it, both feet, legs straightened. This is one step.
4　Use a stop-clock to find how long it takes you to do
　　(a)　10 steps,
　　(b)　50 steps,
　　(c)　100 steps.
5　Draw out a results table like the one overleaf, and fill in your own data.

6　Plot a graph of number of steps against power.

What kind of line do you get? What does this tell you?

A	B	C	D	E	F
Body weight, N	Step height, m	No. steps	Work, J (=A×B×C)	Time, s	Power, W (=D÷E)
		10			
		50			
		100			

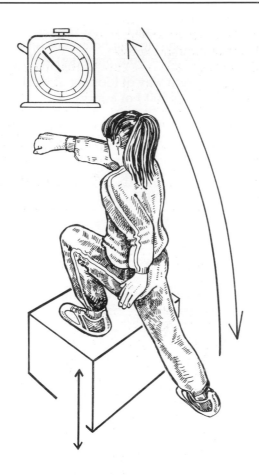

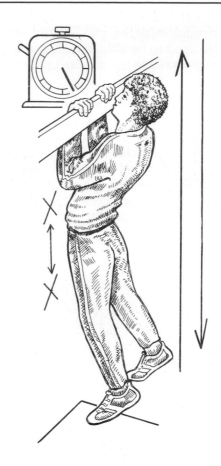

Pull-ups

Pull-ups (or 'chins') concern a very different set of muscles.

1   Fix a beam, so that you can't reach it when standing on the floor.
2   Jump up and catch hold of the beam.
3   Get someone to start a stop-clock as you pull yourself up until your chin reaches the beam.
4   Measure the time you take for
   (a)   2,
   (b)   5,
   (c)   as many as you can do.
5   During one of your pull-ups, get your partner to measure how far up your centre of gravity moves.
6   Produce a table like this, and fill in your own results:

A	B	C	D	E	F
Body weight, N	Height pulled, m	No. pulls	Work, J (=A×B×C)	Time, s	Power, W (=D÷E)
		2			
		5			

Again, you can plot a graph of pull-ups against power. Is the result similar to step-ups?

Press-ups

Press-ups use another set of muscles. You can do ordinary press-ups, or, if you have parallel bars, 'dips'. Again, you need to measure how far your centre of gravity moves, and how many you do in a given time. The results can be recorded in the same way.

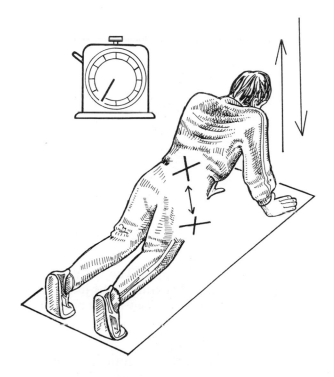

Testing fitness

Some idea of fitness is given by the resting heart rate. Heart muscle increases in strength and efficiency as a result of regular exercise. The volume of the heart also increases. This means that the same amount of blood can be supplied with fewer beats. The heart of a trained athlete therefore beats less often, but more strongly.

cardiac output
(*blood pumped per minute*)
= stroke volume
(*blood pumped per beat*)
× heart rate
(*beats per minute*)

So, the fitter you are, the lower your resting heart rate, although other factors such as age and body type have an effect. Average adult heart rate is about 72 beats per minute; an athlete's may be as low as 30.

Investigation

You can check the truth of this by means of a simple survey.

1 Take the resting pulse rate of a group of people, the same age and sex.
2 Record each in a table according to whether they
   (a)   never take exercise,
   (b)   take occasional exercise,
   (c)   take regular exercise.
3 Find the average pulse rate for each group.

Sample results:

Group	a	b	c
Pulse rates (beats/min)	84 80	60 72	44 53
	76 80	76 66	60 46
	80	62	48
Average			

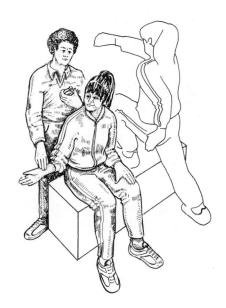

But the resting heart rate does not give enough information. We need to know what happens during exercise, and, just as important, how long it takes to return to normal. These values are the basis for an *index of fitness*. One version of this is the *Harvard step test*, using the kind of step-ups described earlier.

Harvard step test

1 Find a bench or box 0.5 m high.
2 Step up and down, about every 2 s for five minutes.
3 Rest for 1 minute.
4 Get someone to count your pulse for 30 s.
5 After 30 s pause, count pulse for 30 s again.
6 Another 30 s pause, then another 30 s count.

7   Make a result chart like this, and work out
your index of fitness.

*Length of exercise	:	s	300
Multiply by 100	:	(A)	30000
1st pulse count	:		60
2nd pulse count	:		50
3rd pulse count	:		40
Add together	:		150
Multiply by 2	:	(B)	300
Divide A by B	:	(A÷B)	100

This is your *Index of Fitness*. An example is given.

The higher the number, the fitter you are:

90+	80–89	70–79	60–69	50–59
superior	excellent	good	fair	poor

*Note: if you become exhausted, stop and record the
exact time; use this in the calculation.*

Harvard step-test: short form

There is a simpler version of the Harvard step-
test:

$$\text{Index of fitness} = \frac{\text{exercise time (s)} \times 100}{5.5 \times \text{pulse count}}$$

Count your pulse rate from 1 to $1\frac{1}{2}$ minutes after
exercise.

Tuttle pulse-ratio test

This test is rather like the Harvard step-test. It
involves counting step-ups and measuring pulse
rates.

1   Take sitting pulse for 1 minute (A).
2   30 step-ups in 1 minute onto a 33 cm high
    stool.
3   Stop.
4   Take pulse for 2 minutes (B).
5   Tuttle ratio = B/A.

The test tends to favour people with high resting
pulse-rates, but results do improve measurably
with training.

Cooper's test

This test involves simply measuring the distance
which can be walked and/or run in 12 minutes. It is
closely related to the efficiency of the heart and
blood circulation.

Boomerang and Burpee tests

These are tests of agility, of mobility, rather than
of heart and lung function.

The Burpee test

Burpee test
This does not involve running. The Burpee test is
done by continuously repeating a star jump
followed by a squat thrust. How many burpees can
be done in 10 seconds?

Boomerang run
The attempt in 1988 by Steve Cram and Sebastian
Coe to run round the Great Court of Trinity
College, Cambridge while the clock was striking
twelve was a test of agility as well as speed. The
boomerang run test is a much shorter distance but
has more corners:

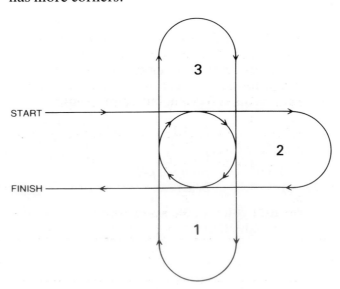

Bicycle ergometer

Athletes can have their fitness checked by a machine called a bicycle ergometer, which works on similar principles to the exercise bike shown above. The athlete works against a measured force and the work done is compared with the oxygen consumption, which is also measured. The main features are shown in the diagram below.

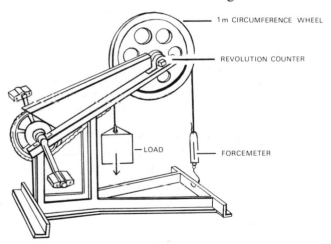

1m CIRCUMFERENCE WHEEL
REVOLUTION COUNTER
LOAD
FORCEMETER

1 Note the reading on the forcemeter, at rest.
2 *Either* count the number of revolutions in a given time, *or* time a certain number of revolutions.
3 Take another forcemeter reading while pedalling.
4 Subtract the forcemeter readings; this gives the pedalling force.
5 Use a table like this for your results:

Food and energy

We have seen that physical work requires energy, and we know that energy comes from food. Values for common foods and sporting activities are shown below.

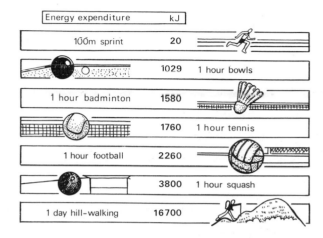

Energy expenditure	kJ	
100m sprint	20	
	1029	1 hour bowls
1 hour badminton	1580	
	1760	1 hour tennis
1 hour football	2260	
	3800	1 hour squash
1 day hill-walking	16700	

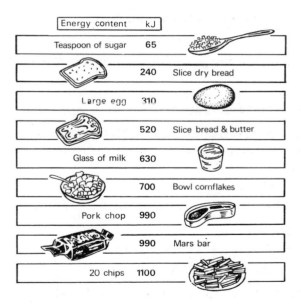

Energy content	kJ	
Teaspoon of sugar	65	
	240	Slice dry bread
Large egg	310	
	520	Slice bread & butter
Glass of milk	630	
	700	Bowl cornflakes
Pork chop	990	
	990	Mars bar
20 chips	1100	

Energy taken in as food, but not used, is stored. Normally, it is stored as fat, so, if the body's shape and condition are to be maintained, intake and output of energy must balance.

A Force, N	B No. revolutions	C Work, J (=A × B)	D Time, s	Power, W (=C ÷ D)

Japanese sumo wrestlers eat more than 7 kg of steak every day, and just look at the daily menu for Oxford oarsmen in training for the boat race:

Breakfast	Lunch	Dinner
2 bowls cereal	Thick soup	Paté and toast
350cm³ orange juice	Pizza	350 g steak,
4 sausages, bacon,	Heavy pudding	potatoes, vegetables,
fried bread, tomatoes,		Pudding
sweet tea		Sweet lemon juice
Extra: up to 10 Mars bars!		

Most people's needs – sports participants or not – are rather less. The daily energy requirements at different ages are shown below:

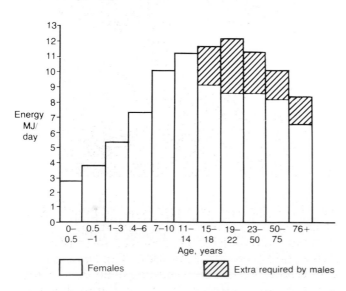

N.B.
1   These are recommended levels for those of average build doing light work.
2   During pregnancy and while breast-feeding, a woman may need an extra 1–2 MJ per day.

Nutritional advice for young athletes:
- Eat a wide variety of foods
- Maintain ideal body mass
- Avoid too much fat (especially saturated fat and cholesterol)
- Eat carbohydrate as starch rather than sugar
- Reduce intake of sodium–e.g. *Losalt*
- Drink large amounts of water

Beware advertisements!

Carbohydrate/glycogen loading

This is a method of storing more carbohydrate (as glycogen) than normal in the muscles. This is particularly useful to runners of marathons and other long distances.

Time, days before race	Action or diet	Result
7	extreme activity	glycogen stores used up
6 to 2	diet of fat and protein only; no carbohydrate	stores remain empty
1	large carbohydrate intake	extra glycogen stored, about twice normal

The graph compares what usually happens during the normal glycogen loading method (line c) with

(a)   if the stores are not emptied first,
(b)   if the 'no carbohydrate' period is left out.

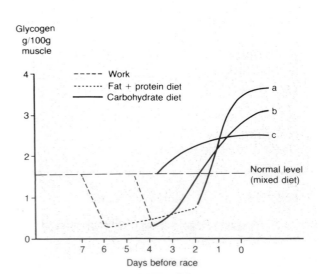

Training

The first training session at the start of a season usually leaves aching muscles. It may even be difficult to walk, especially down stairs. Many muscles will have done little work for a long time. As training becomes more frequent and regular, these aches vanish, and the muscles become more efficient.

Although all sports require a level of general fitness, each sport or group of sports has its own needs. The four main elements of fitness –

endurance flexibility speed strength

– are illustrated.

Strength

Endurance

Flexibility

Speed

Some of these need different types of muscle. For example, the *explosive* sports – sprinting, throwing, jumping etc. – depend on fast twitch fibres and anaerobic respiration. The *endurance* events such as marathon running need slow twitch fibres respiring aerobically. A number of sports – squash, for example – require elements of each.

National athletics coach Frank Dick has produced a useful diagram to show how various types of fitness are related to each other, shown overleaf.

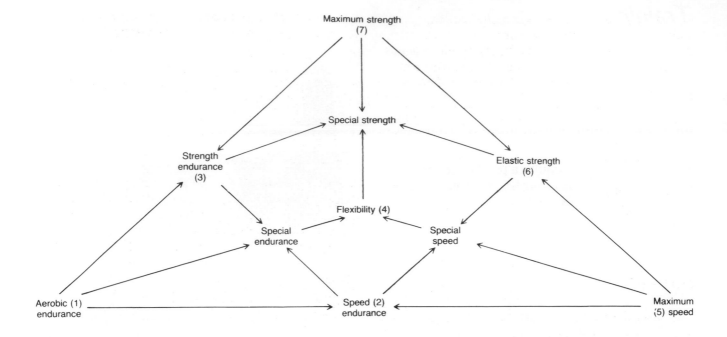

Maximum strength (7)

Special strength

Strength endurance (3)

Elastic strength (6)

Flexibility (4)

Special endurance

Special speed

Aerobic (1) endurance

Speed (2) endurance

Maximum (5) speed

Each kind of fitness has its own suitable training methods:

- **endurance** aerobic   jogging, fartlek, aerobics (1)
                  speed   intensive speed work (2)
                  strength circuit training (3)
- **mobility**   stretching exercises (4)
- **speed**   fast technique practice (5)
- **strength** elastic   standing jumps, medicine ball (6)
                           weight training (7)

Aerobics

Aerobics actually does improve aerobic endurance: heart and lung function, circulation and slow twitch fibres. Because women have a lower oxygen uptake capacity it is important that aerobic endurance is emphasised in the training of any female athlete. Does this explain the recent popularity of aerobics among young (and not so young) women?

Jogging, despite some poor publicity following the premature death of proponent Jim Fixx, remains popular among both sexes. Like aerobics, it is good for aerobic endurance training.

Sir Jimmy Savile

In addition, such exercise can help to convert body fat into lean tissue, i.e. muscle. While diet alone can reduce body mass it may result in a loss of muscle as well as fatty tissue. The table shows the result of one experiment to investigate this.

Regimen	Body mass, kg	Body fat, kg	Lean tissue, kg
Diet, −1 MJ/day	−5.2	−4.2	−1.1
Exercise, 1 MJ/day	−4.7	−5.6	+0.9
Diet, −0.5 MJ/day plus Exercise, 0.5 MJ/day	−5.4	−5.8	+0.4

Injuries

Injuries are an accepted hazard in most sports. In some (motor-cycling) they may be fatal. In others (boxing) they are inevitable. In most sports they are simply more or less frequent, more or less severe.

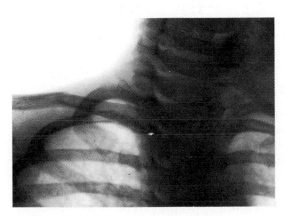

An X-ray showing a fractured clavicle

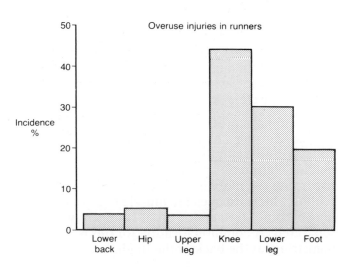

Most injuries are a minor, temporary inconvenience. A few cause retirement.

Many are caused by overuse. These include stress fractures, skin damage, joint injuries, tendon and ligament strains and muscle injuries. The distribution of overuse injuries in runners is shown in the graph.

Cartilage

Cartilage is the material which protects the ends of bones from damaging each other. But if it is torn, so that it becomes broken or separated, it may need to be removed. This most common knee operation is usually spoken of simply as a cartilage operation. Damage happens most frequently in the knee, as it is the knee joint which is most strained by running, jumping or skating.

Cartilage damage may cause the knee to lock or to give way, and it may click when moved. Swelling and pain are also symptoms.

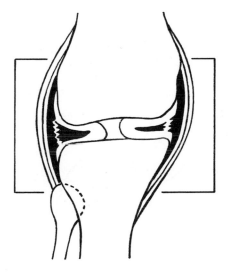

CARTILAGE DAMAGE IN KNEE

Fractures

Fractures are the most dramatic kind of injury. They can be classified in two main ways:

A	closed	skin stays intact
B	open	skin broken

They can also be classified by the way in which the bone breaks, as shown below.

a	transverse	break straight across
b	oblique	break at an angle
c	greenstick	break only part way across
d	impacted	pieces locked into each other
e	comminuted	more than two pieces.

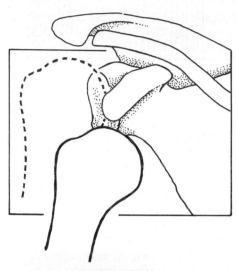

Fractures may be caused by

(i)   a direct blow, e.g. a kick;
(ii) an indirect blow, e.g. falling and landing on the heels can fracture the spine;
(iii) muscular contraction, e.g. a split patella while jumping.

Most common fractures during sport are:

(a) *Colles'* fracture of the radius near the hand, caused by landing on the wrist, e.g. goalkeeper;
(b) fractures of the *clavicle* (collar bone) during a rugby tackle or a fall;
(c) fractures of the *tibia* and *fibula*, e.g. a soccer tackle;
(d) *Potts'* fractures of the ankle, caused by twisting the foot, e.g. ski-ing.

DISLOCATED SHOULDER JOINT

Sprains and tears

These are common in most sports. A sprain occurs when a ligament is stretched or torn, but not with enough force to dislocate the joint. Sprains are most usual in the ankle, where landing unevenly causes the joint to 'turn over'. Firm bandaging reduces swelling as well as providing support for the sprained ankle. Sprains can be as painful, swollen and bruised as a break. Gentle exercise should be increased as the pain eases.

Muscle injury

Injury of the muscles is not always properly named. There are two main types of injury connected with muscles: haematoma (burst blood vessels and clots within the muscle) and so-called 'pulled' muscles.

Haematoma is produced by a sharp blow to the muscle, causing a blood vessel to burst. Blood collects, and a clot forms inside the muscle, making contraction painful. Pulled muscles do occur, but the more usual site of damage is the tendon which attaches the muscle to a bone. This may become stretched, torn or completely separated. A common location for this is the hamstring, at the back of the thigh.

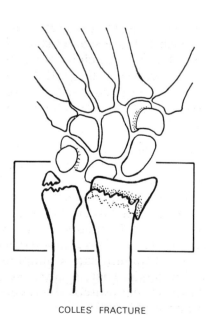

COLLES' FRACTURE

Dislocations

Dislocations can, like fractures, be dramatic. Here, the positions of the bones in a joint are altered by a blow. Most common dislocations are of the shoulder (rugby tackle or fall) and finger joints (oblique blows by balls).

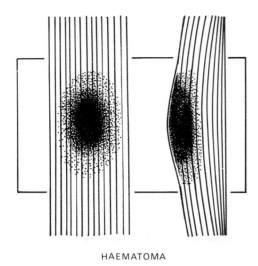

HAEMATOMA

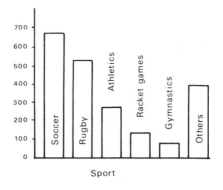

Sport

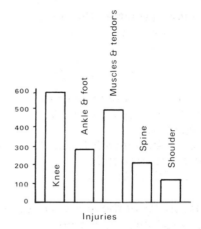

Injuries

Muscle soreness and stiffness can be prevented by exercise routines involving long, low stretching techniques – more like yoga than traditional school PE.

Other symptoms of tendon damage include swelling, thickening or actual splitting. The Achilles tendon above the heel is the best-known for this kind of injury. Others include 'housemaid's knee' (which may affect goalkeepers) and 'tennis elbow'.

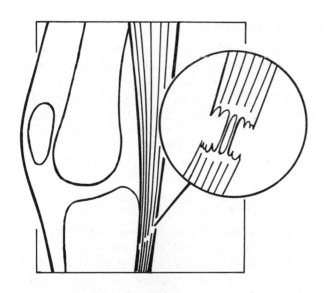

HAMSTRING TENDON INJURY

Sports medicine

Clinics for sports medicine have increased in number in Britain over the last few years. The bar charts show some data from such a clinic at St. James' Hospital, Leeds.

Outside the National Health Service there has been an increase in interest and activity in the field. All Football League clubs, for example, have a physiotherapist on the staff. Some, such as Norwich City, have run courses for local coaches and trainers, in order to spread their specialised knowledge.

Sports medicine has, of course, more to concern itself with than just injuries. The whole realm of fitness, diet, strength, stamina and so on lies in this field. Britain has had in the past a curious attitude towards the highly specialised work done in, for example, East Germany. There every detail of an athlete's body is examined and recorded, so that training can be adapted to his own particular needs. There is even a system of training-down, so that retired athletes do not gain weight in undesired ways.

First aid

With any injury, rapid action may prevent further damage. On the other hand, the wrong action may soon make matters worse. Often, a sportsman may suffer worse injury simply by playing on; or by making a 'comeback' when not fully fit.

It is useful to know not only what to do, but also what *not* to do, when an injury happens.

INJURY	WHAT TO DO	WHAT *NOT* TO DO
Bleeding	Cover wound with sterile dressing, or best material available. Rest; raise wound. If serious, stop bleeding with pressure to wound, and obtain medical aid.	Do *not* apply a tourniquet.
Nose bleed	Sit with head between knees. Pinch bridge of nose; apply ice or cold compress.	Do *not* tilt head backwards.
Fractures:		
tibia	Splint both sides with anything suitable—corner flags and cricket stumps will do! (Or use the other leg.)	
radius	Splint from elbow to knuckles. Make sling from triangular bandage.	Do *not* move unless splint applied. If in any doubt, cover and call medical aid.
clavicle	Pad under armpit, bandage upper arm to chest, sling forearm towards opposite shoulder.	
Dislocations	Support with bandages or sling.	Do *not* try to replace joint without medical help.
Sprains	Apply cold compress, then firm bandage. Raise joint and rest	For ankle sprain, do *not* remove footwear, or swelling may make replacement impossible.
Concussion	Rest and medical aid essential	Do *not* allow to continue to walk home.
Unconsciousness	Turn onto side. Clear mouth of obstruction. Obtain medical aid as soon as possible. On recovery, force to rest.	Do *not* allow to lie on back. Do *not* give anything to drink. Do *not* allow return to activity. Ignore pleas of 'I'm all right; let me back on the field.'
Breathing stops (and heart)	Artifical respiration (and cardiac massage). Loosen clothing; clear throat of any obstruction. Obtain medical aid as soon as possible.	Do *not* wait for medical aid, get the nearest teacher or qualified lifesaver.
Exhaustion	Cover and keep warm. Force to rest. Give sugar or other simple energy source.	Do *not* allow to continue, however keen.
Exposure	Wrap up warmly. Give sugar or other energy source. Gently massage to encourage blood flow.	Do *not* heat up too quickly. Do *not* overwrap head and neck.
Cramp	Stop activity. Massage.	Do *not* continue exercise.

Note: Shock may occur following any injury. There is no specialist treatment for shock. Loosen clothing and force the injured person to rest. Keep them warm.

Infections

Certain infections or diseases are closely associated with sports. Three of them are described here; you may be able to think of others.

Athlete's foot

This condition will be most people's first thought of a sports-linked disease. Athlete's foot is an infection of the skin between the toes. It is caused by a fungus, a kind of ringworm. It is easily transmitted to others by means of towels, socks,

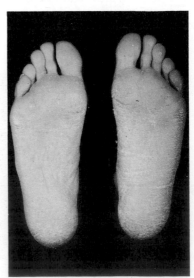

wet changing-room floors. For this reason, swimming pools usually have a disinfectant foot bath outside the changing room, to prevent its spread around the pool.

Verrucas

Verrucas are spread in a similar manner. In this case, though, the hard lumps on the foot are caused by a virus. This is not much affected by disinfectant, so swimming is not usually allowed while the infection persists.

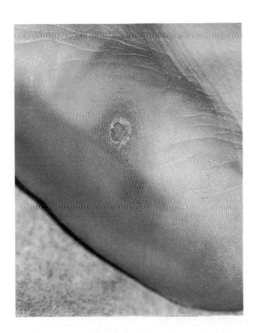

Impetigo

Impetigo is caused by bacteria. It affects the face, where unpleasant yellow vesicles form. It is easily spread by facial contact. Occasionally a whole term's rugby has been lost in schools and colleges when an outbreak of impetigo has occurred among prop forwards!

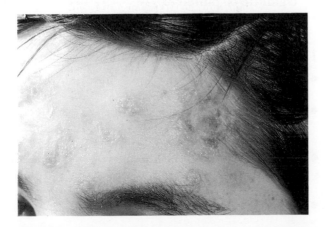

Warming-up

Warming-up has been mentioned as a way of avoiding pulled muscles, particularly the hamstrings. It has the function of gently loosening muscles, rather than suddenly expecting maximum effort from them. It also encourages circulation of the blood to the muscles, rather than, for example, the intestines. And, as its name suggests, it does warm up the body. Muscles do actually work better at 38 or 39° C – about 7 per cent better for each 0.5° C rise in temperature.

Warming-down involves continuous light activity for a few minutes after an event. It maintains a relatively high metabolic rate, and therefore faster removal of wastes – such as lactic acid – from the muscles.

Drugs

England cricketer Ian Botham was banned from first-class cricket for two months in 1986 after admitting – in a newspaper article – to smoking cannabis. (His earlier conviction for the same offence had brought only a reprimand.) There was much resulting discussion of the tobacco and alcohol consumption of the England selectors.

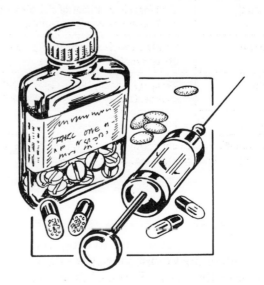

Many sports have introduced drug testing, although not always with great enthusiasm. For example, the Football Association did not reveal the results of the first tests until after the end of the season. Yet a British player had been found using a forbidden stimulant in the 1978 World Cup. The LTA first tested during Wimbledon 1986 but announced that it would take no action against any offenders!

Athletics is generally thought to take the drugs issue seriously. Olympic medals have been taken from guilty competitors who have then been banned for 'life'. However, several have been allowed to compete again after a year or two. There has also been concern over the random tests. Some 'clean' athletes (who are known to be very much opposed to drug-taking) seem to be tested rather frequently, perhaps hiding some of the culprits.

World and Olympic champion Carl Lewis has for a long time suggested that many outstanding performances are assisted by drugs. Though not, perhaps, directly helping on the day of the world record or championship win. Instead, drugs may enable athletes to train harder and for longer periods. The disqualification of Ben Johnson after the 1988 Olympic 100 m final was for taking just this type of drug: *stanozolol*, an anabolic (muscle-building) steroid.

Bob Beamon had no need for drugs – just the thin air of Mexico City – for his incredible record. Lewis himself is striving to break this long-standing, long-jumping record.

Not drugs, just thin air

The attitude of sport science to drugs is clear: 'If science can help athletes more than drugs, then why take drugs?'

Smoking and fitness

One of the most heavily used drugs in our society is tobacco.

Cigarettes and smoking have a peculiar relationship with sport. A casual glance at the lists of sports sponsors might suggest that smoking is an ideal activity for sportsmen. At various times there have been:

Cricket	John Player League
	Benson & Hedges Cup
Rugby Union	John Player Cup
Golf	Picadilly World Matchplay
	Championship
Motor Racing	John Player Special (a car)
	Marlborough McClaren
	(also a car)
Snooker	Embassy World
	Championships

And how many soccer managers can be seen puffing instructions to their teams?

But, in fact, we know that smoking 'takes your breath away'. Few serious athletes smoke during training. There is good scientific evidence that the ability to undertake strenuous exercise is reduced by smoking, however young the athlete may be.

Investigation

Indirect evidence can be got by simply looking at the products of a cigarette:

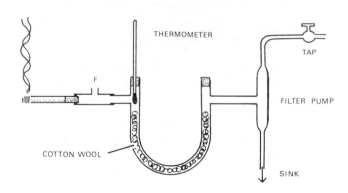

1 Set up the apparatus as shown.
2 When hole F is covered with a finger, the cigarette is 'inhaled'. Cover the hole to light it.
3 Cover and uncover the hole, so that the cigarette is 'puffed'.
4 Look at the cotton wool and the thermometer. What do you notice?

The main ingredients of cigarette smoke are:

- **Tar**. This is the dark brown material which collects on the cotton wool.
- **Irritants**. These cause coughing, and affect the natural cleaning processes of the bronchial tubes.
- **Nicotine**. This affects the nervous system. It is a drug, a stimulant at low doses, a sedative at high doses.
- **Carbon monoxide** has the quickest effects.

Normally, haemoglobin in the blood carries oxygen:

haemoglobin + oxygen = oxyhaemoglobin

However, haemoglobin seems to 'prefer' carbon monoxide. Unlike its reaction with oxygen, carboxyhaemoglobin does not split up again. Once formed, the haemoglobin is unable to carry oxygen.

haemoglobin + carbon monoxide
→ carboxyhaemoglobin

Up to 10 per cent of the oxygen-carrying capacity may be lost in this way in the blood of smokers.

Direct evidence comes from studies on students and servicemen. Examples of results from such studies are:

- Time taken to complete cycling exercise is reduced by stopping smoking.
- Endurance and capacity for exercise is reduced in proportion to the number of cigarettes smoked.
- Improvement produced by training is less in smokers than in non-smokers.

Can't even play blow football now!

In a recent survey of 1559 League footballers, the *British Journal of Sports Medicine* found that only 78 (5 per cent) were smokers. There was a slight difference between Division 4 (6.9 per cent) and Division 1 (3.2 per cent).

Problem page

- Design and make a working model of the human ear bones which will vibrate and amplify sounds.

- Devise a system of floodlights for the school hard-court area, or improved lighting for the sports hall.

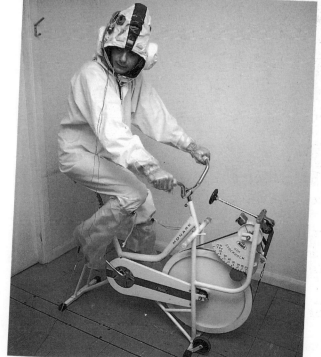

- By doing activities wearing a nylon cagoule it is possible to collect and measure the sweat produced.

   Use this as the basis for an investigation.

   CARE: *This must be done under supervision and carried out for short periods only.*

'Mechanical' sports

In certain sports, the human athlete is of much less importance than a machine. We can think broadly of three kinds of sport.

1 Those which need nothing other than the 'pure' human participants, such as running and wrestling.
2 Those which need a few simple items, such as cricket or tennis, high jump or shot putt, fencing or weightlifting.
3 Those which depend totally on machines. In this chapter we shall look at five of these: motor racing, sailing, cycling, gliding and rowing.

Motor racing

The drawing shows the aspects of a racing car which we can look at fairly simply in scientific terms. The first is the conversion of energy, from chemical energy to kinetic energy, from fuel to power.

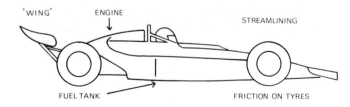

The production of movement in an engine is a bit like the process which occurs in our muscles. Carbon and hydrogen bound up in the fuel are burned in oxygen to give carbon dioxide, water and large quantities of energy. This energy appears as useful kinetic energy, and also as waste heat energy.

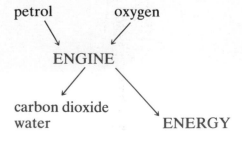

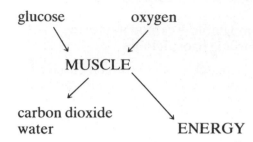

The forces acting on a racing car are complex; some are shown in the diagram:

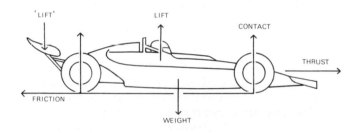

The engine produces thrust, which pushes the car forwards. This is opposed by friction, acting mainly between the tyres and the track, but also within the car itself. There is also air resistance (or *drag*) working against the thrust. The weight of the car (produced by the force of gravity) is opposed by the contact force. The *aerofoil* design reduces drag, but tends to lift the car. Recent developments have seen, firstly, the 'wing' which gives downward *lift* (!) and then a fundamental redesign of the car to provide a net downward force (known as *ground effect*). All the forces must balance in favour of thrust, if the car is to travel forward well and efficiently at high speed.

Investigations

A car moving at constant speed in a straight line has its forces balanced. If it is well designed and well-made, there should be no difficulty for the driver. As soon as either the speed or direction changes, other forces come into effect. More stress is put on the car. Problems, including accidents, happen when cars are accelerating, cornering or braking. Two investigations will give some idea of these difficulties, and the extra forces involved.

1   Set up the track so that the trolley runs freely along it, without needing a push.
2   Clamp the ticker-timer at the top of the track.
3   Attach the tape to the trolley, making sure that it will move freely through the timer.
4   Switch on, and release the trolley from the top of the track.
5   Look closely at the pattern of dots on the tape. Cut it into convenient portions, every 5 (or 10 or 20 etc.) dots – *not* equal lengths.
6   Stick the pieces side by side in the right order, as in the example shown.

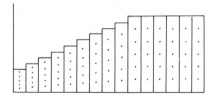

The 'graph' which this produces shows the change of speed caused by gravity. Scientists call this 'the acceleration due to gravity'. Its value is just under $10\,\mathrm{m\,s^{-2}}$. This means that, under the influence of gravity, an object's speed will increase by 10 metres per second every second. (This is written as $10\,\mathrm{m\,s^{-2}}$.) Of course, the trolley will not accelerate this quickly because of the friction of the track.

You can get other graphs by pushing the trolley, or by stopping it suddenly, or by colliding it with another trolley, or in many other ways. A straight, horizontal line always shows constant speed (no acceleration); a line sloping downwards (from left to right) indicates deceleration, or slowing down. By changing the surface of the wheels and/or the track, you can investigate the effect of friction on speed and acceleration.

For the second investigation you will need to beg or borrow (not steal!) a set of model electric racing cars.

1   Find the mass of a car.
2   Use a small forcemeter to find the force needed for the car to just move.
3   With the mass in kg (from g, divide by 1000) and the force in N, the acceleration is given by the equation

$$\begin{array}{ccc} \text{Acceleration} & = & \text{Force} \div \text{Mass} \\ \mathrm{m\,s^{-2}} & & \mathrm{N} \qquad \mathrm{kg} \end{array}$$

4   Set up a simple circuit, and find the highest speed at which the car stays on the track while cornering. This is best done with photo-cells and an electronic timer, but can be done with a stopwatch.
5   Try to find ways of increasing this speed: banking the bend, adding mass ('Plasticine') to the rear of the car, roughening the tyres to increase friction, etc.

Cycling

The modern racing cyclist has very little area in contact with the ground. Balance is therefore a major problem, made worse by the small mass of the machine, compared with the rider. This results

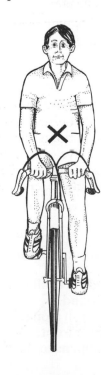

in a high centre of mass, and low stability. When the cyclist is cornering, the forces in operation are complex.

By calculating the forces involved it can be shown that the maximum possible cornering speed depends on the radius of the corner and the angle of the lean. This angle is, however, limited by the amount of friction between the wheel and the track. Tight corners of cinder tracks cannot be taken as quickly as gentle bends on tarmac. On banked corners, the slope of the banking becomes the most important factor.

Gliding

Recent racing cars have made much use of aerofoils in their designs. Firstly, they were used simply to reduce drag; later they were designed to keep the high-speed cars on the track. Gliders use the aerofoil principle for the opposite effect: for true, upward lift. It's quite easy to show how the aerofoil produces such lift:

Investigation

1 Take a sheet of paper.
2 Fold it in half, but do not crease it.
3 Stick one end a few centimetres in from the other end.
4 Make a hole through the centre of each half.
5 Pass a thread through the holes, so that it can move freely.
6 Hold the thread vertically between thumb and fingers of each hand.
7 Spin around, or run along, holding the pointed end of the wing in front.
8 Notice what happens to the 'wing'.

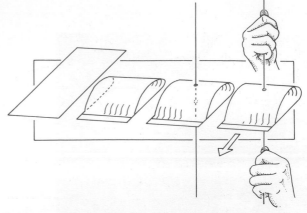

The principle of the aerofoil is straightforward. Air passes both over and under the wing. The air over the curved top has further to travel than the air under the relatively flat base. If the air flow is to be streamlined, and the wing is to stay stable, these two parts of the air must reach the back of the wing at exactly the same time. The air passing above the wing must, therefore, travel faster. Faster air has less pressure. With less pressure above the wing than below it, the wing must rise.

(If the wing is upside down, the air going underneath will have greater speed, and less pressure. The wing will then move downwards. This is what happens in the racing car design.)

Like albatrosses and buzzards, gliders make use of *thermals* for gaining height. These thermals are currents of warm air; as warm air is less dense than colder air, it tends to rise. A glider may rise hundreds of metres on such a thermal, and a

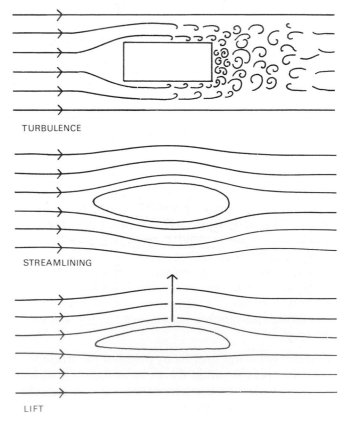

TURBULENCE

STREAMLINING

LIFT

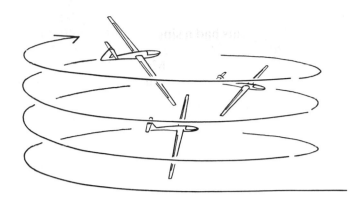

skilled pilot can make use of them to stay up for several hours. The fact that thermals are relatively narrow means that the glider has to circle to stay in the warm updraught. (The longest recorded flight lasted over 15 hours.)

The forces acting on a glider are similar to those on the racing car, although their sizes and their balance are rather different.

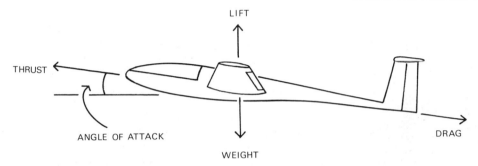

Sailing

It may surprise you to discover that sailing depends on the same basic principles as gliding. The aerodynamics of the movement of air over a curved surface this time apply to the sail. The problem again is similar; to produce enough thrust to overcome the (very large) drag, of the water and the air itself. Solving the problem relies on both hull and sail design.

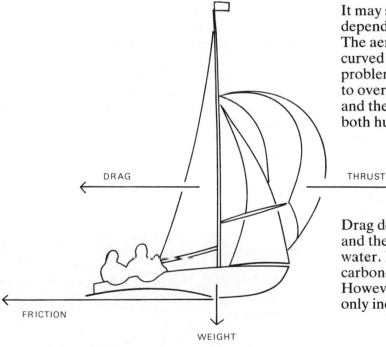

Drag depends on the shape and speed of the boat, and the amount of contact between boat and water. New materials such as fibre-glass and carbon-fibre have improved the shape of boats. However, the increased speed which they produce only increases the drag again.

One way of overcoming this is to reduce the contact area: hence the catamaran (double) and trimaran (triple) hulls.

Early sailing boats had a single, rigid, square sail. This meant using the wind at right angles to the sail to push the boat along. Most children draw boats like this. Such boats cannot, however, sail across or against the wind. A manoeuvre such as *tacking* uses aerofoil principles:

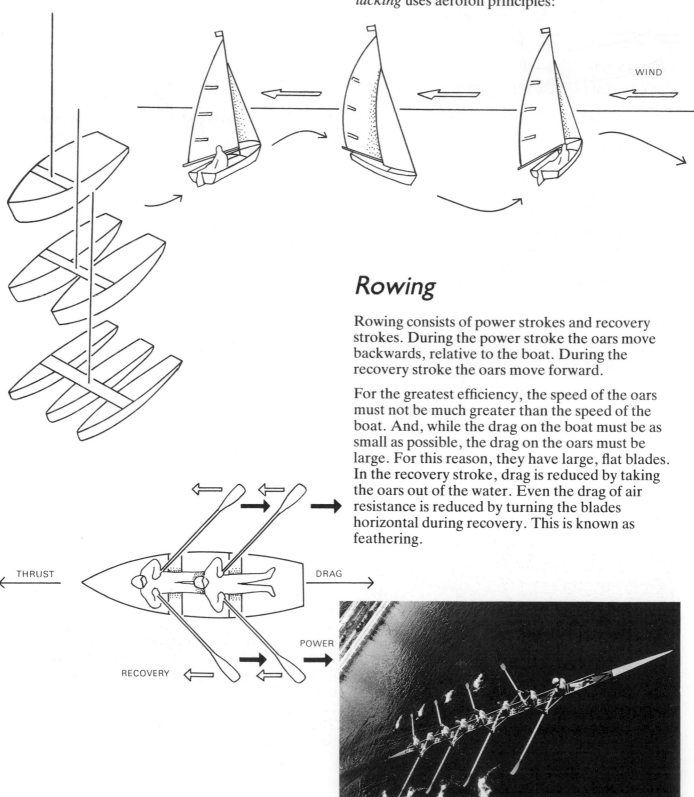

WIND

Rowing

Rowing consists of power strokes and recovery strokes. During the power stroke the oars move backwards, relative to the boat. During the recovery stroke the oars move forward.

For the greatest efficiency, the speed of the oars must not be much greater than the speed of the boat. And, while the drag on the boat must be as small as possible, the drag on the oars must be large. For this reason, they have large, flat blades. In the recovery stroke, drag is reduced by taking the oars out of the water. Even the drag of air resistance is reduced by turning the blades horizontal during recovery. This is known as feathering.

THRUST

DRAG

POWER

RECOVERY

The feathering technique

Human-powered flight

Human-powered flight has long been a dream. Ever since Icarus, people have tried to fly. Most of the early attempts failed because they tried to copy the wrong thing. They tried to build systems which mimicked the flapping motions of the wings of birds and insects. Really, flight is concerned with forward thrust, and an aerofoil shape to convert some of this into lift.

The essential problems of flight are

(a) creating a design to give as much lift as possible;
(b) producing enough power to lift the weight of the body plus the weight of the craft;
(c) being able to maintain the necessary power output for sufficient time, so that 'flight' is achieved, rather than an extended jump.

The overriding difficulty is that increasing the power potential of a human-powered system means a more muscular athlete, and this in turn means more body weight to be carried.

The two graphs give an idea of the problem. Notice the scales on the graphs: three of them are logarithmic, with each mark on the axis being 10 times the value of the previous one. More details about such graphs can be found on page 22.

From the graphs you will see that humans are just on the borderline of the power/weight ratio needed for steady flight, and that even a champion athlete would have trouble in maintaining this rate of work for more than a few seconds.

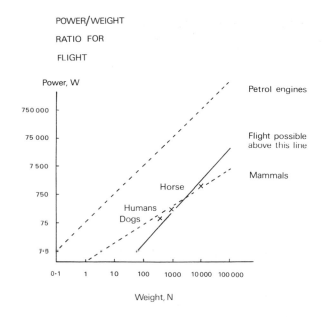

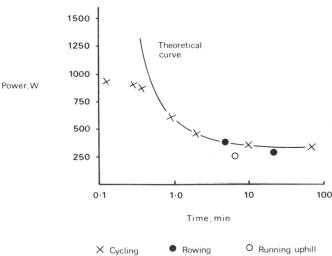

X Cycling   ● Rowing   ○ Running uphill

The Gossamer Albatross

But this is theory. Some thirty years ago, a prize worth today about £60,000 was offered to the first man to make such a flight around a prescribed figure-of-eight course. In 1977, the 'Gossamer Condor' finally succeeded, on August 23, in making designer Paul McCready richer by that amount. Cyclist Bryan Allen carried almost 93 kg (912 N) of which two-thirds was his own body. The later 'Gossamer Albatross' is shown crossing the Channel.

11

Playing surfaces

Ball bounce

We have seen (Chapter 6) how the nature of the ball can affect bounce roll and spin. The playing surface and weather conditions are also important.

If you repeat the bounce experiment, using the same ball on different surfaces, you will get some idea of the effect that the surface has.

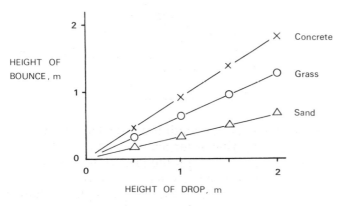

The table gives figures for the bounce of a volleyball on different surfaces.

Surface	e
wood floor	0.76
'Uniturf'	0.75
concrete	0.74
thin mat (25 mm)	0.67
gravel	0.60
grass	0.43
thick mat (200) m	0.42

Lawn tennis, as its name suggests, was at first played only on grass. Today, there is a variety of

Surface	Bounce	Effect of rain
Grass	fast, low	slippery, ball skids
Concrete	fast, high	drains
Clay	slow, high	dries quickly
PVC	slow, high	dangerous
Nylon	fast, low	dangerous

surfaces: grass, concrete, clay, cinders (all outdoors); wood and synthetic plastic materials (mostly indoors). Each of these has its own features.

Cricket talk is full of phrases about the state of the pitch: 'sticky wicket', 'taking spin', 'green on top', 'caught on a drying wicket'. There is, in fact, a surprising amount of 'give' in even the hardest pitch. This elasticity means that the ball bounces higher than might be expected, and slows down. On a soft wicket, the ball bounces awkwardly as it rises and slows.

Running tracks

Running tracks, like tennis courts, may be made from a variety of materials. Each of them has its advantages and its disadvantages.

Grass

Grass is common in schools. It has advantages in that it allows different kinds of footwear, is fairly easy to maintain, and can be taken over by other pitches when not used for running. Its major problems are that it is very slippery when wet, and may get worn away to bare soil.

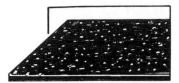

Tarmac

Tarmac drains and dries easily. Athletes are, however, only able to wear soft shoes, and can be badly hurt in a fall.

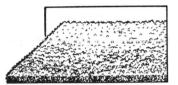

Cinders

This is the traditional surface. It combines durability of tarmac with a softer surface, but is easily waterlogged.

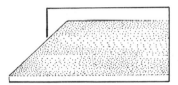

Synthetic materials

Synthetic surfaces such as the 'tartan' track, have recently been developed in an attempt to combine the best features of all the other types. There have, however, been problems with these.

In the Montreal Olympics, there were several accidents in the distance events. These were blamed on the fact that the track was 'silent'; runners could not hear others close behind them. And a tragedy was narrowly avoided when a hammer bounced off the track near a group of runners.

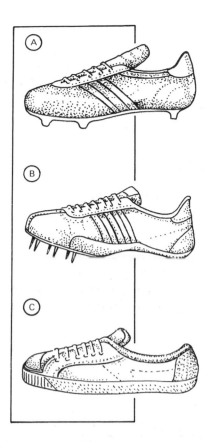

Abnormal weather conditions (such as a severe winter) and artificial surfaces (such as Astroturf) have served to highlight the importance of suitable friction. Too much friction makes movement difficult. Too little friction and the slightest change of speed or direction becomes dangerous.

As with the cornering cyclist, the turning sportsman on foot can only lean so far. The angle of lean depends on the amount of friction between his contact foot and the ground.

Footwear and friction

Sports footwear must provide (a) support and (b) suitable friction.

There are three basic types of sports footwear:

- studded boots – soccer, rugby etc.;
- spikes – athletics;
- tennis/training shoes – hard surfaces and indoor games.

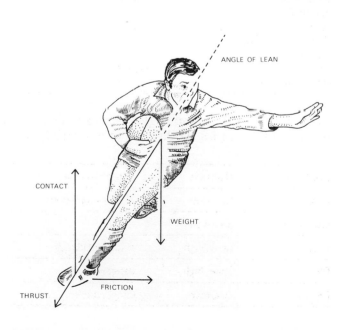

Friction between footwear and surfaces can be estimated by dragging the shoe or boot across the surface with a forcemeter. The frictional force is read just as the first movement occurs.

Friction and tyres

Friction is a doubly important force in motor racing. In the engine, and other moving parts, it is an enemy, fought with lubricating oils. On the track, as the wheels spin, just the right amount is needed for the tyres to grip the track. Too little, and the car slips and slides as if on ice. Too much, and the car slows down.

Racing cars normally have several sets of tyres, for use in different weather conditions, and on different surfaces. If the track is wet, tyres with deeper treads are used. If it dries out during a race, there is a rush to the pits to change to smoother tyres.

Wet weather tyres

Dry weather tyres

Winter sports

Nowhere is friction more critical than in winter sports.

The most important factors in winter sports are friction, balance, and the ice or snow itself.

Ice has two useful properties:

(a)   low friction;
(b)   it melts under pressure.

Both of these can be shown quite simply by two experiments.

Investigation – friction

1   Support a plank on a jack and block so that it is perfectly level.
2   Put an ice cube on the plank at the jack end.
3   Carefully raise the jack until the ice slides.
4   Measure the number of turns of the jack, and/or the angle of the plank.
5   Compare the results with those of other materials, such as wood and metal – and with balls (Chapter 6).

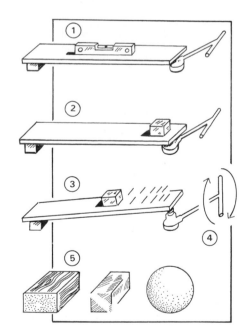

Investigation – regelation

1   Clamp a block of ice firmly.
2   Attach weights to a length of wire.
3   Place the wire across the block.
4   Watch carefully.
     The pressure of the loaded wire melts the ice, and it moves downwards through the ice.
     Above the wire, the pressure is less, and the ice reforms – this is called *regelation*.

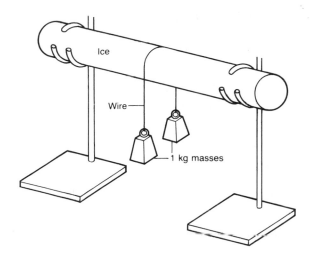

This effect is made use of in both skating and ski-ing. The very thin edge of the skate blade produces a large pressure. (Pressure increases as force on a given area gets larger or area gets smaller.) Heavy skaters and thin blades both produce larger forces.

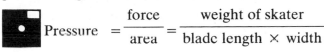

$$\text{Pressure} = \frac{\text{force}}{\text{area}} = \frac{\text{weight of skater}}{\text{blade length} \times \text{width}}$$

This pressure compares with about $50\,000\,\mathrm{N\,m^{-2}}$ for an average man, $200\,000\,\mathrm{N\,m^{-2}}$ for an elephant.

You should find that, even for a light (600 N) skater on the full blade (3 mm × 30 cm), the pressure is more than the elephant. If the skater is skating a figure, the edge of the blade may be as thin as 0.1 mm. This gives an enormous pressure.

The very high pressure melts the ice, and means that skating takes place on a thin film of water. This has extremely low friction. There must, however, be some friction; otherwise, there is no thrust, and no movement.

Thrust in ski-ing is provided by the sticks/poles. Friction is reduced by rubbing wax underneath the skis.

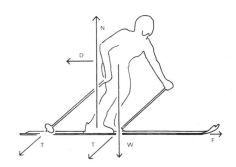

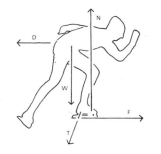

Wear and tear

All surfaces wear away. Some, like grass soccer pitches, wear a lot. Others wear only a little. There are two main factors:

(a) the material of the playing surface;
(b) the spread of activity.

Two examples will illustrate this second factor – running and soccer.

Firstly, on a running track, the lanes are used unevenly:

If an 8-lane track was used for one race at each distance, each with 8 runners, the equivalent of 355 athletes would run on the inside lane of the home straight. The outside lanes of the back straight would be used only once!

Race, m.	Lanes used
100	All, home straight only
200	all, 2nd half of circuit only
400	All
800	All for first bend, then inside lane only
1 500	Inside lane only (except overtaking)
5 000	
10 000	

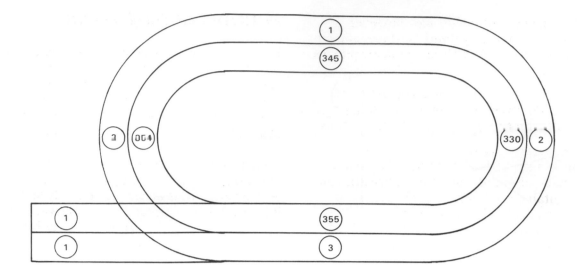

By the spring, most soccer pitches look rather the worse for wear. Analysis of the main areas of activity (Chapter 5) would confirm the evidence of wear. Most play occurs in the penalty areas and centre of the pitch. The diagram shows the most heavily worn areas.

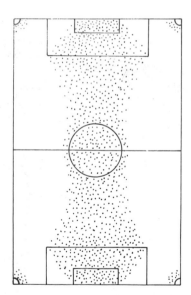

Wear on a soccer pitch

Playing surfaces, the weather and new materials

The winter of 1979 did more than make soccer players learn to skate, or to change their boots during matches. It raised the whole question of weatherproof and/or artificial pitches. Leicester City's 'hot air balloon' system not only protected their own matches, but also enabled the Filbert Street ground to stage three of the Arsenal v Sheffield Wednesday FA Cup replays. Somewhat ironically Arsenal's own under-soil heating was at the time one of the few other protective measures taken by any club. Such a system also keeps grass on the pitch all the year round.

A number of Football League clubs, including QPR and Luton, have installed synthetic pitches. These give the clubs considerable advantages:

- they permit play in virtually all weather conditions;
- the ground can be used for large numbers of matches without damage;
- other sports (e.g. hockey) and other events (e.g. rock concerts) can take place, bringing in extra revenue;
- visiting teams may not be as well adjusted to the pitch.

Several competitions (e.g. the FA Cup) have forbidden the use of synthetic surfaces, and the Football League has prohibited other clubs from converting their grounds. QPR have now (in 1988) reverted to grass.

Artificial ski slope

The 1986 hockey World Cup was, however, played in London on a synthetic surface, and most American Football takes place on plastic pitches, not all of which are green.

With top-class tennis now played on artificial surfaces outdoors as well as indoors, perhaps grass pitches will soon be found only in history books.

Where the weather is too warm for snow ski-ing, artificial ski slopes have been built. There are usually made of tufted nylon (like a brush), and provide suitable friction for learning to ski, or even for advanced skiers to practise on. Most recently, a 'moving carpet' (ever upwards) has removed the need to repeatedly climb to the top!

A new running track

Running tracks have changed, too. We have seen the materials used in the past. The most recent design (at Harvard, USA) is designed to 'bounce' in harmony with the runner. A rubber covered wooden suspension system supports the fibreglass and steel track. Because it 'gives' with the runner, the contact time is greater. A greater impulse force results, and therefore more speed. A second advantage is that the shock of landing is reduced, and fewer injuries occur, particularly knee injuries. It is estimated that the Harvard track could reduce middle-distance records by several seconds.

Problem page

■ Design and make a device for measuring the grip of different kinds of sports footwear on a variety of surfaces.

What kind of sole is best for all-purpose wear?

■ Use damaged or unwanted equipment to investigate methods of construction and strengths of different material.

■ Find the best fabrics for (a) visibility, (b) wear and tear resistance for use in sports clothing.

Appendix A

Computer programs

1 Reaction time

```
10   MODE 7
20   PRINT TAB(10,1) "REACTION TIME"
30   PRINT TAB(10) "-------------"
40   PRINT'""This program measures your reaction time"
50   INPUT "Please type in your name "N$
60   PRINT'""Press 'RETURN' for instructions."
70   IF GET$<>CHR$(13) THEN GOTO 70
80   CLS
90   PRINT TAB(0,4) "After a random interval"'"the screen will
     go blank."
100  PRINT'""This starts the timer."
110  PRINT'""Pressing the 'SPACE BAR' stops the clock"
120  PRINT'""Your reaction time will then be shown."
130  PRINT'""Press 'RETURN' when ready."
140  IF GET$<>CHR$(13) THEN GOTO 140
150  LET then=RND(300)+150
160  TIME=0
170  REPEAT
180  IF INKEY$(0)=" " THEN GOSUB 310
190  UNTIL TIME>then
200  TIME=0
210  CLS
220  IF GET$="" THEN GOTO 220
230  LET reaction=TIME/100
240  PRINT "YOUR REACTION TIME IS : "'
250  PRINT reaction;
260  PRINT " SECONDS"
270  PRINT'""Another go, ";N$" ?"
280  INPUT '"('Y' or 'N') "Y$
290  IF Y$="Y" THEN GOTO 80
300  END
310  REM * CHEAT CHECK
320  CLS
330  PRINT TAB(0,6) "CHEAT!"
340  PRINT TAB(0,9) "Please wait for screen to go blank."
350  PRINT'""Press 'RETURN' when ready."
360  RETURN
```

2 Predicting the world mile record

```
10   MODE 7
20   PRINT "Predicting the world mile record"
30   FOR D=1 TO 32: PRINT "-";: NEXT D
40   PRINT'""This program uses a formula to try to"
50   PRINT "predict the development of the"
60   PRINT "world mile record."
70   PRINT "You can choose a table ('T')"
80   INPUT "or a graph ('G') "G$
90   IF G$="G" OR G$="g" THEN GOTO 280
100  MODE 3
110  PRINT "    Year", "    Time, min:s"
120  PRINT "    ----", "    ----------"
130  FOR T=0 to 80 STEP 10 : REM 1900 to 1980
140  GOSUB 230
150  NEXT T
160  FOR T=87 TO 98 : REM 1987 to 1998
170  GO SUB 230
180  NEXT T
190  PRINT '"World mile record as predicted by formula    ";
200  INPUT "Enter 'g' for graph: "G$
210  IF G$="G" OR G$='g' THEN GOTO 280
220  GOTO 370
230  LET R=4.777-02039*T+0.000104*T^2 : REM formula
     (decimal minutes)
240  LET S=(R-INTR)*60 : REM whole minutes
250  LET M=INT(S*100)/100 : REM seconds to 2 decimal places
260  PRINT T+1900,INTR;":";M
270  RETURN
280  MODE 1: GCOL 0,2
290  GOSUB 380 : REM graph axes
300  MOVE 180,1000
310  FOR T=0 TO 98
320  LET R=4.777-0.02039*T+0.000104*T^2
330  PLOT 1,T/4,-(R-3.5)*10)
340  NEXT T
350  INPUT "Enter 'T' for table, 'E' to end "T$
360  IF T$="T" OR T$="t" THEN GOTO 100
370  END
380  PRINT "m:s"
390  FOR V=48 TO 0 STEP -4
400  LET Z=1+(48-V)/4
410  PRINT TAB(0,Z);"4:";V
420  NEXT V
430  FOR V=56 TO 36 STEP -4
440  LET Z=14+((56-V)6/V)
450  PRINT TAB(0,Z);"3:";V
460  NEXT V
470  PRINT TAB(4,Z+1);"1900;
480  FOR Y=1 TO 9
490  PRINT " ";Y*10;
500  NEXT Y
510  PRINT " 2000"
520  PRINT '"World mile record: predicted by formula"'
530  RETURN
```

3 Somatotypes

```
10   MODE 3
20   DATA 9,12,15,18,24,42
30   DATA 42,24,18,15,12,9
40   DATA -11,-8,-7,-6,6,7,8,11
50   PRINT TAB(6);"SOMATOTYPES"
60   PRINT TAB(6);"-----------"
70   PRINT "This program plots the position of somatotypes."
80   PRINT "Enter the values for"
81   PRINT "ectomorph, endomorph and mesomorph"
82   PRINT "(each between 1 and 7)"
83   PRINT "and the somatotype will be plotted."''
90   INPUT"Press 'Return' to continue"X$
100  MODE 1
110  VDU28,0,4,35,0
120  GCOL 0,3
130  CLG
140  MOVE 100,250
150  FOR Y=1 TO 6
160  READ X
170  PLOT 1,X*4,100
180  NEXT Y
```

```
190    FOR Y=1 TO 6
200    READ X
210    PLOT 1,X*4,-100
220    NEXT Y
230    FOR X=4 TO 1 STEP -1
240    READ Y
250    PLOT 1,X*-48,Y*5
260    NEXT X
270    FOR X=4 TO 1 STEP -1
280    READ Y
290    PLOT 1,X*-48,Y*5
300    NEXT X
310    VDU5
320    MOVE600,870
330    PRINT "mesomorph"
340    MOVE0,100
350    PRINT "endomorph"
360    MOVE1000,150
370    PRINT "ectomorph"
300    VDU4
390    LET G=1
400    GCOL 0,G
410    INPUT "endomorph: "A
420    INPUT "mesomorph: "B
430    INPUT "ectomorph: "C
440    PLOT 69,580 ! 70*((4-A)*0.87+(C-4)*0.5), 480+40*((4-
       A)*0.5+(B-4)+(4-C)*0.87)
450    INPUT "Again (Y/N)";Y$
460    IF Y$="N" THEN GOTO 500
470    CLS
480    LET G=G+1 : IF G=4 THEN LET G=1
490    GOTO 400
500    END
```

4 Speed of golf ball

```
10     CLS
20     PRINT TAB(6);"Speed of golf ball"
30     PRINT TAB(6);"------------------"
40     INPUT "Mass of club, g    "C
50     INPUT "Mass of ball, g    "B
60     PRINT "Coefficient of restitution (e)"
70     INPUT "(Normally 0.7)        "E
80     LET V=(1+E)*C/(C+B)
90     LET W=INT(100*V)/100
100    PRINT"""The ball will travel ";W;" times"""faster than the
       club."
110    INPUT ""Another go ('Y' or 'N') "Y$
120    IF Y$="Y" OR Y$="y" THEN RUN
```

5 Pressure of ice skates

```
10     CLS
20     PRINT TAB(6);"Pressure of ice skates"
30     PRINT TAB(6);"----------------------"
40     INPUT "Weight of skater, N :    "W
50     INPUT "Length of blade, cm :    "L
60     INPUT "Thickness of blade, mm :    "T
70     LET P-W/((L*T)/100000)
80     LET I=INT(P/100000)
90     PRINT ""Pressure of blade on ice = "'I;" × 10^5 N/m^2"
100    FOR J=1 TO 4 :PRINT: NEXT J
110    PRINT "Another go ('Y' or 'N') "
120    IF GET$="Y" THEN RUN
130    END
```

6 Surface area

```
10     CLS
20     PRINT TAB(6);"Surface Area"
30     PRINT TAB(6);"------------"
40     INPUT "Name :   "N$
50     INPUT "Your mass, in kg :   "M
60     INPUT "Your height, in metres :   "M
70     GOSUB 320 : REM calculation
```

```
80     PRINT'""Your surface area, ";N$", is "'S;" square metres."
90     PRINT '''
100    PRINT "Another go ('Y' or 'N')";
110    IF GET$="Y" THEN RUN
120    PRINT """Press 'T' to see tables of sample data";
130    IF GET$="T" THEN GOTO 150
140    END
150    CLS
160    PRINT "Mass, kg","Height, m","Surface Area, m^2"
170    LET Q=0
180    FOR M=25 TO 100 STEP 5 : REM masses 25 to 100 kg
190    FOR H=1.4 TO 2 STEP 0.1 : REM heights 1.4 to 2.0m
200    GOSUB 320 : REM calculation
210    PRINT M,H,S
220    LET Q=Q+1
230    IF Q=19 THEN GOSUB 270
240    NEXT H
250    NEXT M
260    END
270    INPUT '"Press 'RETURN' for more"Q$
280    LET Q=0
290    CLS
300    PRINT "Mass, kg","Height, m","Surface Area, m^2"
310    RETURN
320    LET A = M^0.425*(100*H)^0.725*0.00718 : REM formula
330    LET S - INT(A*100)/100 : REM area
340    RETURN
```

7 Centre of mass

```
10     MODE3
20     PRINT "Centre of Mass"
30     PRINT "--------------"
40     PRINT "This program performs the calculation "
50     PRINT "for finding the centre of mass "
60     PRINT "by lying on a plank"
70     PRINT "resting on platform (bathroom) scales."''
80     INPUT "Name :      "N$
90     INPUT "Length of plank, m :      "L
100    PRINT "Your weight, ":N$;","'"in newtons :
       ";:INPUT ""N
110    INPUT "Force of plank, N :      "K
120    INPUT "Force with you on plank, N :   "P
130    LET G=L*(P-K)/N
140    LET C=INT(100*G)/100
150    PRINT '""Your centre of mass, ";N$;", is "'C;" m above
       your feet."
160    FOR J=1 TO 4:PRINT:NEXT J
170    INPUT "Another go ('Y' or 'N') ";Y$
180    IF Y$= "Y" OR Y$= "y" THEN RUN
190    END
```

8 Harvard step test

```
10     CLS
20     PRINT TAB(6);"Harvard Step Test"
30     PRINT TAB(6);"-----------------"
40     INPUT "Length of exercise, min:
50     LET A=0
60     FOR F=1 TO 3
70     PRINT "30s pulse count after ";F;" min. rest:";
80     INPUT    "P
90     LET A=A+P : REM add counts
100    NEXT F
110    LET I=INT(L*60000/A/2)/10 : REM calculation
120    PRINT '"Fitness index = ";I'
130    IF I>90 THEN LET I$="superior"
140    IF 79<I AND I<90 THEN LET I$="excellent"
150    IF 80>I AND I>69 THEN LET I$="good"
160    IF 70>I AND I>59 THEN LET I$="fair"
170    IF I<60 THEN LET I$="poor"
180    PRINT '"This is ";I$
190    PRINT "Another go? ('Y' or 'N')"
200    IF GET $="Y" THEN RUN
210    END
```

9 Projectiles

```
10   ON ERROR GOTO20
20   MODE3
30   PRINT "Projectiles"
40   PRINT "-----------"
50   PRINT "This program displays the flight path of a
     projectile (object, ball or person)."
60   PRINT "It gives the maximum height and distance before
     plotting a graph."
70   INPUT'''"Enter 'B' for ball, 'O' for object (e.g. discus), 'J' for
     jump. "G
80   IF G$="B" THEN LET I=0.8:LET J=5:LET D=70:LET
     M=500:LET W$="release, ":GOTO120
90   IF G$="O" THEN LET I=10:LET J=100:LET D=19: LET
     M=40:LET W$="release, "GOTO120
100  IF G$="J" THEN LET I=38:LET J=200:LET D=10:LET
     M=10:LET W$="approach, ":GOTO120
110  GOTO70
120  INPUT '''"Press 'Return' to continue"Z$
130  MODE1
140  VDU 28,0,7,35,0
150  LET G=9.81
160  LET C=1
170  PRINT "speed of ";W$;"(0-";D;"m/s) ";:INPUT""U
180  IF U>D THEN PRINT "Too fast! Please press
     'Return'.":INPUT""Z$:CLS:GOTO170
190  IF G$="J" THEN LET H$="take-off, " ELSE LET H$=W$
200  PRINT "angle of ";H$"deg    ";:INPUT""A
210  LET T=A*PI/180 : REM radians
220  PRINT "height of ";H$;"(0-3m) ";:INPUT""H
230  LET
     R=(U^2*SINT*COST+U*COST*SQR((U*SINT)^2+2*G*H))/G
240  PRINT "distance :     ";INT (R*10)/10;" m"
250  LET R=R*I
260  LET S=(U*SINT)^2/2/G
270  PRINT"maximum height :    ";H+INT(S*10)/10;" m"'
280  LET S=S*J
290  INPUT "Press 'Return' for graph"Y$
300  GCOL0,3
310  MOVE900,50
320  VDU5
330  PRINT M;"m"
340  VDU4
350  MOVE0,0
360  GCOL 0,C
370  FOR X=0 TO 1280
380  DRAW X, SIN(X/R)*S
390  IF SGN(SIN(X/R))=-1 THEN GOTO 410
400  NEXT X
410  MOVE0,0
420  LET C=C+1
430  IFC=4 THEN LET C=1
440  CLS
450  GOTO 170
460  END
```

10 Sprint start

[LOGO (*Controller*), using *Driver* interface]

```
TO RACE
RESET
START
FINISH
END
```

```
TO START                      Checks for false start until gun
DOUNTIL [CHECK]                 is fired.
   [INPUTON? 1] GUN
END
```

```
TO CHECK
IF INPUTON? 2 [MAKE "LANE      Examines each lane in turn to
   2 ALARM]                      check that foot is still on
IF INPUTON? 3 [MAKE "LANE        starting block. If necessary,
   3 ALARM]                      selects correct alarm.
IF INPUTON? 4 [MAKE "LANE
   4 ALARM]
IF INPUTON? 5 [MAKE "LANE
   5 ALARM]
IF INPUTON? 6 [MAKE "LANE
   6 ALARM]
IF INPUTON? 7 [MAKE "LANE
   7 ALARM]
END
```

```
TO ALARM
REPEAT 10 [SWITCHON           Sets off alarm for appropriate
   :LANE PAUSE 0.2             lane.
SWITCHOFF :LANE PAUSE
   0.2]
END
```

```
TO GUN
SWITCHON [1 8]               Fires 'gun'. Starts clock.
PAUSE 0.1                      Checks for impossibly quick
CHECK                          start. Turns off 'gun'.
SWITCHOFF 1
END
```

```
TO FINISH
DOUNTIL [PAUSE 0] [NOT        Stops clock when light beam
   INPUTON? 8] SWITCHOFF 8     is broken.
END
```

Key to Devices:
Input	Output
1 starter switch	1 start buzzer/bell
2–7 starting blocks	2–7 warning lights
8 finish beam detector	8 clock

Appendix B

References & Further Reading

Beashel, P & Taylor, J	*Sport Examined*	Macmillan 1986
Brodie, DA & Thornhill, JJ	*Microcomputing in Sport and Physical Education*	Lepus Books 1983
Buchanan, D	*Greek Athletics*	Longman 1976
Diagram Group	*Book of Comparisons*	Sidgwick & Jackson/Penguin 1980
Diagram Group	*Rules of the Game*	Bantam 1976
Diagram Group	*Sports Comparisons*	Arthur Barker 1982
Dick, FW	*Sports Training Principles*	Lepus Books 1980
Edington, D & Edgerton, V	*The Biology of Physical Activity*	Houghton Miflin 1976
Grosser, M	*Gossamer Odyssey*	Michael Joseph 1981
Hay, JG	*Biomechanics of Sports Techniques*	Prentice Hall 1978
Lindsay, BI	*Sports Records as Biological Data*	*J. Biol. Ed. (1975) 9, 86–91*
McWhirter, N	*Guinness Book of Records*	Guinness 1990
New Scientist	Olympic Special, No. 1415, 2	August 1984
Page, RL	*Man and Machines*	Pergamon 1975
Page, RL	*The Physics of Human Movement*	Wheaton 1978
Thomas, V	*Exercise Physiology*	Crosby, Lockwood, Staples 1975
Wells, CL	*Women, Sport and Performance*	Human Kinetics Publishers 1985
Williams, JPR (Ed.)	*Sports Injuries Handbook*	Collins Willow 1987

Appendix C

National Curriculum (Science) Attainment Targets

Chapter

	1	2	3	4	5	6	7	8	9	10	11
AT1	*	*	*	*	*	*	*	*	*	*	*
AT2	*										
AT3				*	*		*	*	*		
AT4			*	*	*						
AT5											
AT6				*		*					*
AT7										*	
AT8						*					
AT9										*	
AT10				*	*	*				*	*
AT11		*			*						
AT12	*	*		*	*	*	*				
AT13					*			*	*		
AT14					*		*				
AT15					*		*				
AT16											
AT17		*									

List of Attainment Targets

1 Exploration of science
2 The variety of life
3 Processes of life
4 Genetics and evolution
5 Human influences on the Earth
6 Types and uses of materials
7 Making new materials
8 Explaining how materials behave
9 Earth and atmosphere
10 Forces
11 Electricity and magnetism
12 IT and microelectronics
13 Energy
14 Sound and music
15 Using light and electromagnetic radiation
16 The Earth in space
17 The nature of science

Appendix D

Examination questions

1 Give reasons for each of these practices:
   (a) Warming-up before playing or competing.
   (b) Putting on a track-suit (or similar clothing) when resting after exercise.
   (c) Not eating immediately before exercise.
   (d) Not going into bat directly from a dark pavilion.
   (e) Taking salt tablets after strenuous exercise.
   (f) Bending the knees when landing on the floor from a trampoline.

2 These results were obtained during a study of the effects of practice on taking penalty kicks.

Attempt	1 2 3 4 5 6 7 8 9 10 11 12 13 14 15
Result	G M G M G G G S G G G S S G G

G = goal; M = miss; S = save

   Is there any evidence of a practice effect on (a) the kicker, (b) the goalkeeper?

3 Why will A balance, but B and C fall over?

4 (a) What is the average resting body temperature?
   (b) Why is it wrong to refer to it as 'normal'?

   (c) What happens to body temperature during exercise?
   (d) How is a relatively constant temperature maintained?

5 The drawings are traced from photographs of three stages in a golf shot.

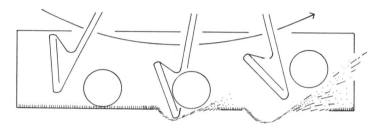

   (a) What kind of club is being used?
   (b) State three ways in which the original photographs may have been taken.
   (c) Will the ball as drawn spin clockwise, anti-clockwise, or not at all?
   (d) How will it bounce on landing?

6

Time, s	Force, N	
	Front foot	Rear foot
0	0	0
0.1	750	1 110
0.2	700	0
0.3	800	0
0.4	1 000	0
0.5	0	0

   The table shows the forces applied by each foot to the starting blocks during a sprint start.
   (a) Draw a graph to show the relationship between time and force for each foot singly, and both feet added together.
   (b) Describe, in words, what happens to the forces.

7 Would you use a barchart, histogram or graph to show each of these?
   (a) Olympic marathon times, 1908–84
   (b) Number of medals won by each country
   (c) Numbers of batsmen scoring 0–49, 50–99, 1–149, 150–199, 200+ in a Test Match

(d)   Number of passes before each goal in a hockey match

(e)   Size of crowd at a football ground each Saturday

(f)   Time of each runner in a race

(g)   Amount lifted compared with body mass of each weightlifter.

8   What are the main reasons for error in
(a)   timing a 100 m race?
(b)   measuring a discus throw?
(c)   judging gymnastics?

9   The table gives the dimensions of three different rackets. Draw a scaled sketch of each, and identify them.

Racket	A	B	C
Overall length, cm	65	69	69
Length of shaft, cm	41	47	38
Width of head, cm	20	19	23.5

10   Each of these statements about energy is incorrect. Write a corrected version of each statement.
(a)   Protein provides more energy per kg than any other food.
(b)   The SI unit of food (and other kinds of) energy is the Watt.
(c)   A pork chop contains as much energy as is used up in running up a flight of stairs.
(d)   The conversion of chemical energy to kinetic energy takes place in the liver.
(e)   When a golf ball flies through the air, it has both potential and light energy.
(f)   Lifting 10 N a height of 5 m needs 2 J of energy.

11   In a training session, an athlete repeatedly lifts a 100 N load from the floor to her shoulders.
(a)   If her shoulders are 1.5 m from the floor, how much work does she do in a single lift?
(b)   How much work does she do in 100 lifts?
(c)   If the 100 lifts take 5 minutes, how much power does she develop?
(d)   Why should all such weight training be supervised?

12   Footballers are often spoken of as having 'cartilage operations'.
(a)   Draw a healthy knee joint, showing cartilage.
(b)   What is the function of cartilage?
(c)   How may it be damaged?

(d)   What is done in such a 'cartilage operation'?

13   (a)   Which arm bones are in similar positions to these leg bones?
(i) femur, (ii) tibia, (iii) fibula.
(b)   Which leg bone has no 'relative' in the arm?

14   Explain why
(a)   a bowler (cricket) polishes one side of the ball
(b)   squash players have a long 'knock-up' before play
(c)   snooker players put chalk on their cues
(d)   golfers don't use smooth balls.

15   (a)   Draw a sketch of a section through the eye.
Label: cornea, lens, iris, pupil, retina, blind spot.
(b)   What changes take place in the eyes as a sportsman watches a ball coming towards him?
(c)   Explain these phrases:
(i)   having a good eye;
(ii)   keeping your eye on the ball;
(iii)   getting your eye in.

16   How can we tell that energy is lost in
(a)   the impact of cricket bat and ball?
(b)   the repeated hitting of a squash ball?

17   Details of a recent England cricket team are listed:

Player	Bats- (-handed)	Bowls (-arm)
Chris Broad	left	—
Graham Gooch	right	right
Bill Athey	right	—
David Gower	left	—
Mike Gatting	right	right
Ian Botham	right	right
Bruce French	right	—
John Emburey	right	right
Neil Foster	right	right
Phil Edmonds	right	left
Graham Dilley	left	right
	LEFT: 3	LEFT: 1
	RIGHT: 8	RIGHT: 6

In the population as a whole, about 10 per cent are actually left-handed. Could this be true of the cricket team above? (Remember that left-handed people may bat right-handed and right-handed people left-handed!)

18   The graph shows how the maximum amount of oxygen which can be taken in varies with age.

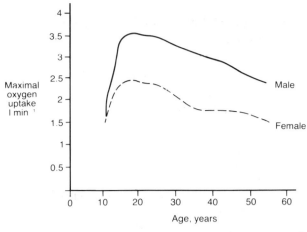

(a)   At what age is oxygen uptake greatest?
(b)   When is there the smallest difference between males and females?
(c)   Describe (i) the changes with age, (ii) the difference between the sexes.

19   Muscles contain a number of enzymes which carry out essential processes. Many of these are concerned with the release of energy. Some take part in anaerobic respiration, others in aerobic respiration.

Two important muscle enzymes are PFK and SDH. Their proportions in the leg muscles of different runners is shown, together with the amount of *slow twitch* muscle fibre.

Runner	PFK	SDH	% slow fibres
distance	15	8	75
middle-distance	27	5	65
sprinter	28	4	26

(a)   What is the difference between *anaerobic* and *aerobic* respiration?
(b)   Which of the enzymes and which type of muscle seem to be used in aerobic respiration?
(c)   What is produced during anaerobic respiration which makes it suitable only for short periods?

20   The ground staff want to water an area of new turf without soaking the rest of the grass.

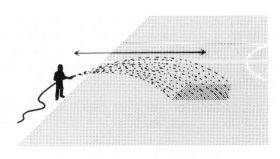

The distance (d) travelled by the water is related to its speed (s) and the angle of the hose (a) by

$$d = s^2 \sin 2a/g$$

(where $g = 9.81\ ms^{-2}$, acceleration due to gravity).

Find (a)   the lowest possible speed if the target is 15 m away;
     (b)   the best angle for the same target if the water speed is $20\ ms^{-1}$.

21   With the help of the diagram, explain why a cornering cyclist does not (usually!) fall over.

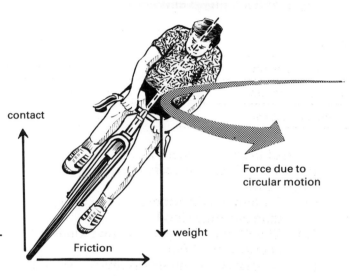

contact

Force due to circular motion

weight

Friction

Explain what happens if
(a)   the tyres are worn;
(b)   the track is wet;
(c)   the cyclist is heavier;
(d)   the bicycle is lighter;
(e)   the cyclist takes the corner more slowly.

22   Find the surface area of a person 160 cm tall with a body mass of 80 kg.

What height would a person of 65 kg body mass need to be to have the same surface area?

23   The table shows the heights of the gold
      medallist (male) in races at a recent Olympic
      Games.

Event	Height of winner, m
400 m	1.854
800 m	1.803
5 000 m	1.727
marathon	1.702

(a)   Choose *either* a bar chart *or* a line
      graph, and display these findings.
(b)   Describe the pattern.
(c)   Predict the height of the winner of the
      200 m.
(d)   An athlete's stride length is normally
      1.15 times his/her height. Calculate the
      stride length of the 400 m winner.

Index